Suddenly Claire
wanted to scream

"You want, you think, you know." Claire stamped her feet and stormed, "What about me? Am I to have no say at all in this mockery of a marriage?"

Rolf remained seated, the dawning of a twinkle in his eyes. "Our marriage is a mockery only because you have made it so, *chérie*. Yet I am not despondent. I see before me a woman slowly emerging from a cocoon of ice."

Then swiftly he moved to stand beside her, holding her chin and tilting her head to study her furious profile.

"There is hope for us yet," he breathed. "You are angry, you are disheveled, you smell ever so slightly of goat—yet never have I seen you looking more beautiful, more desirable, more warmly human!"

Marriage by Capture

by

MARGARET ROME

Harlequin Books

TORONTO • LONDON • LOS ANGELES • AMSTERDAM
SYDNEY • HAMBURG • PARIS • STOCKHOLM • ATHENS • TOKYO

Original hardcover edition published in 1980
by Mills & Boon Limited

ISBN 0-373-02369-3

Harlequin edition published November 1980

CHAPTER ONE

SMOKE drifted from candles set in sconces fashioned from silver dug out of the island's own mines. Cutlery set out upon the tastefully arranged dinner table was stamped with the three-legged emblem of the Kingdom of Man. Manx crystal fashioned into wine goblets radiated a myriad sparkles with each twirl of a stem, and napkins made of linen spun and woven in the kitchens of isolated cottages stood out crisply white against a flower arrangement of bell-shaped fuchsia, the late-summer flower that ran riot, splashing rich red and purple colour down hillsides, along hedgerows and inside every town and country garden.

Pictures tracing the island's past were ranged around panelled walls, Viking longboats braving fierce seas, packed stem to stern with wild-eyed men wearing horned helmets, who had descended upon the island to sack, plunder and harry before settling to stamp their names and influence upon its people, then in order of succession came portraits of every Scottish king and English lord who had proclaimed himself ruler of the tiny piece of land whose size and location had left it vulnerable to invasion from neighbouring English, Scottish, Irish and Norse raiders.

A clue to the direction in which the allegiance of the Manx people lay was betrayed by the girl act-ing hostess at the foot of the table. Over a dress of white, expensive simplicity she had draped a sash of tartan that no Celt would immediately have recognised, a check as individual as the inhabitants of Man, containing colours purple as the heather, green as the fields, gold as the gorse, white as the cottages, and blue as the sea surrounding their miniature kingdom.

As Claire looked up to glance the length of the dinner table her eyes were caught and held by her father's frowning signal of displeasure. She bit her lip to suppress the answering grimace of resentment that threatened to disturb the flawless serenity of her expression, nevertheless slight colour rose in her father's cheeks when he recognised a hint of disdain in grey eyes levelling a return of censure over the heads of their unsuspecting guests. Garff Reginald Foxdale was not used to rebuke, however mutely extended. He was accustomed to laying down the law to everyone and not least his unshakably poised, infuriating self-possessed daughter.

Having become highly sensitive to her father's reactions, and knowing full well that the objective behind this important dinner party could be gained or lost depending on the nature of his disposition, she decided to employ diplomacy and directed towards him one of the swift, rare smiles which since early childhood had never failed to achieve a desired result. As she had calculated, he reacted favourably, taken unawares once again by the miracle sweetener she reserved for just such fraught occasions, one that had to be used extremely frugally in order to retain the element of surprise, the impact of the unexpected, in the smile her father had likened to flame bursting from the heart of a diamond, and once—more waspishly—to dawn, firing, probing, melting the sharply-frozen profile of a glacier.

The remark had hurt, as did the reminder. On impulse she turned to her companion, seeking assurance.

'Jonathan, do people consider me to be a cold, unfeeling person?' she blurted, then immediately regretted her weakness.

'Certainly not, my dear.' Though prompt, his reply was boringly predictable.

Ashamed of harbouring disloyal thoughts about the man she was pledged to marry, she shrugged and attempted to dismiss the subject completely. 'It was a silly question,' she forced a light laugh. 'Father's glowering looks must be having more effect than I had imagined—I don't usually indulge in moody introspection.'

She was made unaccountably furious when he nodded agreement. 'You do seem to be rather on edge this evening,' he considered thoughtfully. 'Don't make a habit of it, will you, my sweet? I rely upon your calm, steadying influence, the unruffled aplomb that makes you stand out in a crowd—like royalty, you exude an air of supreme dignity, a touch-me-not quality that one must inherit, as it can never be successfully emulated.'

He did not seem to realise that he had just contradicted his previous denial. Her lips parted to

prótest, but before she could speak she became conscious once more of her father's condemning eyes
reminding her of her duties. Father really is in-
sufferable, she thought, composing her features before directing him a brief nod of acknowledgement.
He demanded so much of herself, yet displayed little
personal effort. Her position as one of the island's
most successful society hostesses was unshakable, yet
tonight she had taken extra pains in order to de-
termine the success of the evening's party. Guests
had been carefully chosen to ensure that the com-
pany was congenial; hours had been spent arrang-
ing the table, deciding who should sit next to
whom, and already she had been complimented
upon the excellence of the food and accompanying
wines. Yet in spite of her efforts conversation was
desultory—at times, even forced—and for this she
blamed her father's ridiculous insistence upon
standing on ceremony with their North American
guests.

She felt tempted to allow him to strangle in his
own etiquette, but then, after a glance at Charity
MacLeod's unhappy face, she changed her mind.

'I hope you'll enjoy your stay on the island, Mrs
MacLeod—no doubt you're finding it quite a contrast to your native Montreal?' she questioned
politely.

Eagerly, her guest grabbed at the conversational
lifeline. Smiling her gratitude, she begged in an
attractive Transatlantic drawl, 'Please call me
Charity! Although I have no personal connection
with your island, I've heard many stories passed on
by each generation of my husband's family about

the homeland that was never forgotten, even though it's over a hundred years since the first MacLeod emigrated to Canada. Which is why, when we landed here, I felt able to share Duncan's feeling of being an exile arriving home.'

Her husband, a bluff, kindly man who had somehow managed to retain a Scottish lilt to his tone, added with a chuckle, 'And we're merely the forerunners—there are many more to follow! There's a flourishing Manx-Canadian club in our Province, and when we heard of the plans afoot to celebrate a thousand years of the Parliament of Tynwald, the oldest assembly in the world, and of the island's wish to welcome as many exiles as possible to its shores, the appeal was irresistible.' With a twinkle in his eyes he turned to Claire's father. 'Are the islanders prepared, sir, to suffer once more a horde of Scottish invaders?'

Garff Foxdale's smile remained austere. Projecting a dry type of hauteur that Claire deplored, he managed to reduce Duncan MacLeod's attempted humour to the level of impertinence. 'Our guests will not be here on sufferance, Mr MacLeod. Whether their roots be Celtic, Scottish, English or Scandinavian is secondary—indeed, as a perusal of our island's history will verify, though the origins of a man might lie in any one of those four cultures he can still claim to be of genuine Manx descent. My own family, the Foxdales, can trace back its lineage one thousand years to the first Norse invaders, yet,' his proud head tilted, 'I consider myself to be first and foremost a Manxman.'

Duncan MacLeod could so easily have resented

such a show of patronage. Claire had no idea what
status he had achieved in his adopted country, but
knowing that her father's aim was to interest as
many wealthy exiles as possible in a scheme to
benefit the island, the presence of Duncan MacLeod
at their table was indicative of a background of
financial security.

But much to Claire's relief, he accepted with a
good-humoured nod when his host proffered cigars
and brandy. Correctly interpreting this action as a
signal for the ladies to retire, she rose to her feet.

'Shall we take coffee in the drawing-room, ladies?
I suspect that the gentlemen wish to indulge not
only in brandy but also in weighty conversation, so
I vote we leave them to it.'

With an alacrity born of long practice, her aunt
Effie seconded the motion, with the result that
Charity MacLeod found herself whisked from the
dining-room, ensconced in a comfortable chair sip-
ping coffee from a fragile porcelain cup, before
quite realising how it had come about.

Her bemused eyes followed Claire's movements
as she sank on to a couch and leant back a head that
seemed burdened by a coiled, braided coronet of
flaxen hair. All evening she had tried not to stare
at the girl who was so supremely beautiful, who
moved with such regal grace, but at that moment
she felt unable to resist the temptation to enjoy a
visual feast.

Mere seconds elapsed before Claire became
aware of her concentrated stare. Delicately, her
eyebrows arched, impelling Charity to respond to

her mute enquiry. Made to feel ill-mannered by the
girl who at first meeting had prompted within her
a ridiculous impulse to curtsey, she cast about
wildly in her mind for some subject of diversion.

'I'd like to thank you, my dear,' she drawled, 'for
the concern you showed when you suspected that
my husband might have been feeling slighted. You
needn't have worried, however—my Duncan
wouldn't be where he is today had he lacked the
protection of a hide thick enough to excite the envy
of an elephant!'

Shame on her father's behalf brought a slight
tinge of colour to Claire's cheeks. 'My father has
an unfortunate tendency to appear austere and
abrupt, but it's quite unintentional,' she assured
her guest with quiet dignity. 'As an important member of Manx society his responsibilities are heavy,
and though I've urged him many times to relax,
his mantle of authority has become so much a part
of him it seemingly can't be discarded.'

Charity nodded acceptance of the polite apology,
but had to strangle an impulse to urge Claire to act
upon her own advice, to unfreeze, to become less
of a 'cat that walks alone' so that she might be
accepted among the ranks of happier, less perfect
mortals.

'Is he a member of the nobility?'

Claire and her aunt exchanged smiles, amused
by such snobbery. Mainly in an attempt to main-
tain Charity's illusions, but also spurred on by
family pride, Effie leapt delicately to her brother's
defence.

'Nordic customs were never allowed to die out completely on the island, which is why I can safely claim that the Foxdale strain has remained pure throughout the centuries. It owes its purity to the fact that, in the preliminaries leading up to courtship and marriage, the most interested parties played a very minor part. The negotiations were carried on by others—on the side of the girl, by her family, and on the side of the man by a representative who might have been either a friend or a relative. In an effort to keep the racial strain pure from contamination only *partis* whose suitability—decided by social position—were introduced to each other, any inequality being an absolute bar. This rule was rigidly observed almost until the present century, so you see, Mrs MacLeod, though the Foxdale family can no longer lay claim to a title, its heritage of social distinction is unassailable.'

Charity trained an enormous round-eyed stare upon Claire's amused face. 'And is that the way it happened with you?' she breathed, awestricken, busily filing in the archives of her mind, to be unearthed for the benefit of her friends back home, details of quaint Nordic customs being practised by the Manx people *right up until the present day*! 'Was *your* fiancé hand-picked by your father with the object of maintaining the purity of the Foxdale blood-line?'

Claire recoiled from the crude suggestion. Her lips parted to voice an objection, but the denial died to a gasp on her lips as, like a flashback from the past, she recalled the commencement of her courtship, the manner in which her father had kept her isolated from youngsters of her own age until, without any preliminaries, on her nineteenth birthday Jonathan Heywood and his parents had been invited to dinner. Wrestling with feelings of shocked incredulity, she began unearthing from her mind other incidents that slotted together forming a picture of conspiracy that was as unbelievable as it was shocking.

With one innocent, breathless question Charity MacLeod had ripped the blinkers from her eyes, revealing how stupidly ingenuous she had been in her belief that her father's approval of her dates with Jonathan had stemmed from the realisation that she had reached maturity and was entitled to a life of her own, that in his cold, dispassionate way he was trying to atone for imprisoning her in solitude during the joyful years of her teens, a time when, like a bird, she should have been free to soar. No wonder she had been grateful for any youthful companionship—however dull, however predictable, however *lukewarm* ...

Mercifully, the reappearance of the men saved her the effort of a reply. She felt certain that her eyes were betraying shock, that her face looked ashen and her mouth pinched with pain, but when the shrewdly observant Charity showed no sign of reacting she breathed a sigh of relief. Grateful, this once, for her father's teaching of rigid self-discipline, she turned towards the door, ready to resume her duties by greeting her guests in the composed tranquil manner of an expert hostess.

The business proposition her father had planned
tentatively to outline to Duncan MacLeod must
have been well received, Claire thought, noting his
almost affable expression as he took the seat next to
Charity, prepared to indulge in polite conversation.
Jonathan, too, seemed pleased with the outcome
of their brief talk. With eyes that had become suddenly hyper-critical, she watched him approach,
but was unable to fault the physical attributes of
the man who was considered to be one of the best
'catches' among their élite social circle. Always impeccably dressed in outfits tailored to fit perfectly
on to his slender frame, he epitomised the image of
a man-about-town, one whose conversation was an
asset to any gathering, a man who belonged to all
the right clubs, who was passably proficient in all
the fashionable recreations.

His background, too, was as faultless as his
image. The only son of a wealthy, distinguished
English-Manx family whose roots in the island extended almost as deep as those of the Foxdales and,
since his father had retired some years previously
leaving him in sole charge of the longest established
law firm on the island, his future seemed comfortably assured.

She sighed when he relaxed on to the couch beside
her, wondering why she felt no leap of the pulses
when his hand clasped hers, why she felt no urge
to caress the fair head bending close to murmur in
her ear, why she shuddered from a mouth that had
once seemed tender but which she now suspected
was merely weak. It had been this illusion of tenderness, she realised, that had drawn her to him in

the first place. Starved of love and affection since the death of her mother, she had been ready to fall into the arms of any man displaying qualities directly opposed to those of her father.

'Miss me...?' Jonathan murmured, then continued without waiting for her reply. 'Old MacLeod seems very interested in your father's scheme. Not only has he implied that he is prepared to give it his personal backing, he has also promised to drum up interest among his friends. One fellow in particular has been mentioned as a sure-fire certainty—a Manx exile like himself who has managed to accumulate more money than can be spent in one man's lifetime.'

She looked up quickly, puzzled by the note of bitter resentment contained in his words. But his expression was bland, his pale blue eyes unworried as they met hers.

Duncan MacLeod's voice boomed across the room 'Charity,' he addressed his wife, 'do you happen to have Rolf Ramsey's telephone number? I'd kinda like to get in touch with him—the sooner the better!'

His wife turned an animated face towards him. 'I sure have! You know I always like to keep tabs on that young man.'

'Ramsey...?' Claire's father looked interested. 'A local name, surely...?'

Claire felt the jolt that stiffened Jonathan's frame. She looked up, and was surprised to see that his face was ashen, with tiny beads of sweat lining his upper lip.

'Surely, Jonathan,' her father continued, 'your

firm has a long-standing client of that name? I remember your father commenting about his eccentricities and the fact that his forebears once farmed at the south end of the island.'

'*Rolf* Ramsey, you said ...?' Jonathan tugged at his collar as if he felt it too tight, then nervously cleared his throat. 'We do have a client of that name. As for his being eccentric—my father was probably referring to the fact that some years ago the farm that had once belonged to his family came on to the market. How Mr Ramsey became aware of this fact we never did discover, but we were instructed to bid for it on his behalf and to buy it whatever the price. This we did, but then,' his voice hoarsened, 'after writing to inform him that the deal had been concluded we were amazed by his further instructions. The farm buildings, which were in a state of disrepair, were to be restored to their original condition, walls repaired, roof re-thatched, all outhouses re-equipped with implements relevant to the tasks for which they'd been used. The interior of the farmhouse itself was to be left untouched, not an ornament displaced, not so much as an item of bedlinen removed.'

Claire found that she was clenching her fists as she sensed his struggle to appear calm while still labouring against the effects of sudden shock. He ran the tip of his tongue around lips that were paper-dry before continuing to satisfy his listeners' avid curiosity.

'Thousands of pounds were spent purchasing equipment which by now had reached the status of antiques. At the beginning we wrote quoting the price of each article and asking if it was satisfactory, but so much correspondence was involved that finally we received a terse note from our client instructing us to buy any relevant article, whatever the price, and that he would settle up with us at the end of each year.'

'What an extraordinarily trusting fellow!' Garff Foxdale interrupted. 'But then,' he quirked dryly, 'he must obviously have known that he was dealing with a firm of integrity.'

'But if the farm has remained empty since Mr Ramsey purchased it, it must surely be once again falling into disrepair,' Aunt Effie queried indignantly.

'A caretaker has been employed to look after the handful of animals, to light the occasional fire so that the house is kept aired,' Jonathan explained.

'But for what reason?' Aunt Effie wailed.

Jonathan shrugged. 'That I can't tell you. Unless ...' Once more Claire detected a resentful tinge to his tone. 'Unless it's simply a case of a rich man indulging a whim.'

'Well,' Duncan MacLeod drawled, 'if your Mr Ramsey is the Rolf Ramsey we know, he can certainly afford to indulge in any whim that takes his fancy. The first Ramsey who emigrated from your shores—probably the original owner of the farm you mentioned—made his pile in the fur trade and successive generations have built upon it, with the result that today Rolf Ramsey is reckoned to be one of the richest men in Canada. And what's more,' he beamed around the astonished assembly, 'you're all gonna have the privilege of meeting him! The

Ramsey's have always been noted for the code they live by—*Never forgive a slight, never forget a favour*—Rolf owes me a favour, which is why I know that if I ask him to, he'll hop over to this island on the first available flight!'

CHAPTER TWO

CHARITY was in a furore of excitement. Tonight they were to attend the ball that was to be the highlight of the island's Scottish Festival, planned to celebrate the traditional and historical links between the Scottish and Manx people. All week the clans had been gathering, and hundreds were expected to attend the ball that was being held to acknowledge the MacLeods as descendants of the last Kings of Man.

Claire stood up to greet her when she erupted into the sitting-room of her home where they had arranged to meet before going on to the ball as a party. Charity was wearing the MacLeod tartan for the very first time—and it showed.

'Claire dear, do I look all right? This will be such a proud evening for Duncan, I'd hate to let him down!'

'You look perfect,' Claire lied, determined to allow nothing to spoil the event the MacLeods would probably talk about for years to come.

'You're sure...?' Anxiously Charity peered into a wall mirror, adjusted her sash, then, seemingly satisfied, turned round to assure Claire, 'I've never seen my Duncan looking more distinguished, he wears the kilt as if to the manner born. But then,' she heaved an ecstatic sigh, 'that's just as it should be, considering his background.'

The image of a portly Duncan rigged out in kilt, sporran and velvet jacket was almost more than Claire's composure could withstand, but somehow she managed to keep at bay the smile twitching at the corner of her mouth.

'You're looking extremely elegant, as usual, my dear,' Charity complimented, beaming approval on an organdie ball gown flouncing fully from Claire's tiny waist, with a strapless bodice that left creamy shoulders bare except for the intrusion of a silken strip of Manx tartan held in place by a brooch of twisted silver. Feeling the strain of her intense excitement, Charity collapsed into a chair and surveyed Claire through half-lowered lids. 'Don't you *ever* feel excited?' she censured in a tone of exasperation.

'No, I don't believe I do,' Claire replied, sounding slightly surprised.

'You will tonight,' Charity promised. 'I've just received some marvellous news—Rolf Ramsey arrived on the island an hour ago and he'll be joining us later this evening!'

'Oh, really...?' Claire did not mean to sound bored, but the prospect of having added to their party yet another overawed Colonial eager to discuss, branch by branch, his particular family tree, was far from invigorating.

Correctly interpreting the blankness of her expression, Charity grinned. 'I know what you're thinking,' she accused, 'just another Canadian! Believe me, my dear, Rolf Ramsey is so much of an individual he could never be classed as typical of any race or creed. Though he's extremely wealthy, he devotes most of his time to the study and preservation of wilderness and consequently has become such an expert that he was approached by our National Parks Service to act as a consultant. His mother, a charming woman of French-Canadian extraction, has often confided her worries about his long sojourn in the northwoods during which he lives rough, eats out of tins, and is at the mercy of ferocious elements. Often she's declared,' Charity smiled, 'that he has a deeper affinity with grizzlies and Indians than he has with civilised society. But she's really very proud of him, but then everyone back home is proud of the Ramseys. She shot upright, as if only at that moment recognising a truth. 'I suppose it was Rolf's ancestor and men like him who created what little history we Canadians possess —you have your kings, your lords, your chieftains, but we have Angus Ramsey and his fellow voyageurs!'

It was still early, they were not due to leave for half an hour yet, so Claire sat down next to Charity and resigned herself to being bored.

'Voyageurs?' she queried politely. 'The term is unfamiliar to me.'

Nothing loath, Charity supplied promptly and with obvious pride, 'Legendary heroes of the northwoods of Canada, freelance trappers and traders who worked their traps alone. Most of them had no interest in the fur trade as such, nor had they any ambitions to be rich or successful in anything other than meeting the endless challenge of the wilderness, hacking their way through dark, austere woods abounding with wild animals, risking their lives in boiling rapids, paddling their canoes for fifteen to eighteen hours a day, barely eating, stopping for mere seconds at the end of each hour for a quick smoke before paddling on in either pouring rain, fierce winds or cruel, blistering sun!

'Usually they had to scout and hack a trail out of the wilderness by themselves, but Angus Ramsey was cleverer than most. He made friends with the Indians and in exchange for treating them as brothers he was allowed to benefit from the experience of generations of hunters who long before had developed their own canoe routes and their own paths through the forests. Most of the trails followed by canoeists today are paths trampled smooth by moccasined Indian feet centuries before the first white man arrived.'

'How very grim!' Claire shuddered. 'Hours of work, very little food, no vestige of comfort—they must surely have been martyrs to misery!'

Charity laughed aloud. 'That's one thing they most certainly were not,' she chuckled. 'It's been recorded that even as the voyageurs set forth in the pre-dawn dark they launched into a rousing chorus that resounded through the pitch-black woods, and they continued singing hour after hour throughout the day and into the evening—sad songs, gay songs, moral songs, and many that were distinctly bawdy.'

Claire suppressed a fastidious shudder. Usually she kept away from the island's capital at the height of the tourist season, nevertheless, on one or two occasions she had witnessed drunken young men thronging the streets late at night singing vulgar songs at the tops of their voices, displaying a lack of decorum she had found disgusting.

'And what of this Angus Ramsey you mentioned —the relative of the friend you're expecting this evening—presumably he made his fortune, then settled in Montreal?'

Charity looked suddenly uncomfortable. 'Not he,' she hedged. 'That course of action has been credited to his son.'

Sensing that there was something Charity did not wish her to know, Claire abandoned good manners to insist,

'But the father, what happened to him?'

Though there was not the slightest possibility of being overheard, Charity cast an anxious look over her shoulder before confessing in a whisper, 'Rumour has it that he made his home with the Indians and married one of their women, who bore him a son ...!'

Dancing was already in progress when they entered the huge ballroom, its walls festooned with tartans of every known Scottish clan, its floor packed with white-gowned, tartan-sashed women and their proudly-kilted partners. A fiddler was leading the band in a spirited reel, and judging from peals of happy laughter novices who had dared to venture on to the dance floor were having as much fun as the experts who were setting an example.

As her father played host, introducing the Mac-Leods to all the notables present, Claire quietly detached herself from the party, hoping she would not be missed until supper was being served, which would not be for another hour at least. Jonathan, who had been caught up in the organisation of the ball, had disappeared behind the scenes to check that all was going well, so, feeling in need of solitude, she made her escape through an opening in heavy velvet curtains screening a deserted balcony.

Unaccountably, she was feeling very much on edge. It was as if every nerve of her body had tensed to combat some unknown challenge. A combination of Jonathan's tension and Charity's silly prattle had unsettled her; she liked life to run on calm, uneventful lines, she liked to mix with ordinary people because they knew what was acceptable and what was not. Unpredictable people upset carefully-laid plans, created disorder, disarray—the sort of conditions her father had never allowed to exist in his household. Up until now there had not been the least hint of upset to the even tenor of her life, so why was she feeling so nervy, jumping at the slightest sound?

She walked to the edge of the balcony and leant her arms on the stone balustrade to gaze dreamily through the deepening dusk at the bay below with its arc outlined by a fringe of coloured lights, at the shadowy bulk of a steamer berthed in the harbour and, just discernible, the tall, swaying masts of fishing boats bobbing gently on the waves. A far cry from the Canadian northwoods! She frowned, wondering why such a thought should have popped into her mind. Charity's fanciful talk was the cause of her unsettled mood, she decided crossly—that, and the prospect of having shortly to cope with an ignorant backwoodsman who she was half expecting to arrive wearing buckskins or a feathered headdress!

'Your island holds a wealth of unsuspected beauty!'

The words stroked across her shoulder in a soft, hypnotic drawl.

Startled, she twirled on her heel, then stood stock-still, a slim core of tension wrapped in an agitated flutter of organdie.

'Who ... who are you?' she gasped—unnecessarily, for somehow she already knew. The jet-black hair, sloe-dark eyes narrowed slightly whilst, arrow-swift, they raked her face; skin tanned as leather stretched across a profile so sharply defined it could have been hewn by a hatchet, were all alien, not of her world. Not even a conventional evening suit draped superbly on a wide-shouldered, lean-tapering frame could subdue her fear of the man towering over her, relaxed, half-smiling, yet exuding animal virility from a power-packed body. Only years of discipline, allied to an unsuspected hint of her father's hauteur, enabled her to project indifference into her tone.

'Mr Ramsey, I presume...?' She extended a surprisingly steady hand to greet him. 'I've been expecting you.'

When a brown sinewed hand enclosed hers she was unprepared for the jerk that jolted her hard against his lean, muscled body. Arms whipped her waist, lashing her tight, then a hungry mouth descended, crushing to extinction the gasp of breathless astonishment on her parted lips. During the terrifying duration of the kiss she felt paralysed by an electrifying current that scorched her mind of thought, her limbs of movement, yet sparked a tingling furor of excitement along every nerve. To her eternal shame she did not struggle, did not cry out, not even when, satiated as a bear after a surfeit of honey, he raised his head to allow her to gasp in great gulps of life-saving oxygen.

'And I've been expecting you.' The quietly-spoken words did not make sense. Neither did the look in eyes that were devouring her face, drinking in every nuance of expression, lingering upon the brush of gold-tipped lashes against flushed cheeks, upon the soft golden crown of hair, upon the trembling mouth that would not be still, then delving finally into the depth of eyes that were grey clouds of bewilderment and fear.

'Don't look so violated, Nordic nymph,' he murmured. 'Why not be honest, and acknowledge that the body has a language all of its own, a signalling system that says: *"You excite me!"* Our eyes met, I read your message and so naturally I responded.'

She jerked out of his reach, scandalised by the allegation. 'Are you daring to imply that I invited your brutal assault?' she stormed, wiping a shaking hand across bruised lips.

His calm smile infuriated her. 'I suppose, you being a product of an over-sophisticated society, your reaction is understandable. It's an established fact that though animals can't speak they have no difficulty in communicating mutual attraction. Humans also possess this faculty, but for some uncomprehensible reason they prefer to pretend ignorance and become indignant if accused of hypocrisy. We felt instant attraction, you and I,' he drawled with easy conviction, 'yet I suspect you're a stickler for protocol, therefore, true to form, you'll insist upon all the proprieties being observed before our urge to mate is allowed to reach the stage of consummation.'

He waited, then, mistaking her look of stunned disbelief for shyness, he shrugged, looked her over carefully, then startled her with the sudden exclamation.

'God, but you're lovely—too lovely to bargain your body for a few meaningless vows and a modest wedding ring. But if that's all it will take to bed you then consider the bargain struck!' When he extended his hand, palm uppermost, as if expecting her to participate in some barbaric ritual of commitment, she decided that she had had enough.

'You're mad, quite mad!' she gasped, then turned on her heel and fled.

She sped indoors in search of Jonathan whose faults had suddenly paled into insignificance compared with the devilish impudence of the man descended from ruthless voyageurs, and found him scanning the dance floor in search of her.

'Where on earth have you been?' His voice had an irritated edge. 'We've waited ages to go into supper.'

Hoping she could trust her voice not to quaver, she told him truthfully, 'I've been talking to Mr Ramsey—the friend of the MacLeods who's just arrived—I believe arrangements have been made

for him to join our party.' Then impulsively she
appealed in a breathless rush, 'Let's slip away by
ourselves for just this once, Jonathan, it's ages since
we've had any time to ourselves!'

But he seemed not to have heard her last jumbled
words. He grabbed her arm. 'You mean Ramsey has
actually arrived on the island?'

'Yes,' she stammered, wondering at the look of
shock that had darkened his eyes. 'Why? What's
wrong, Jonathan, are you in some kind of trouble?'

The question seemed to jerk him to his senses.
With a tight, humourless smile he prevaricated,
'What was that you said about us slipping away?
Good idea—let's get out of here!'

They both turned to flee like quarry from a
hunter, but found Garff Foxdale barring the only
exit. 'So you've managed to find her at last!' Casting a dark frown in Claire's direction, he ushered
them both through the doorway of a room in which
a buffet supper was being served. 'It was most ill-
mannered of you to keep everyone waiting,' he told
Claire severely. 'Be quick, both of you, choose what
you want to eat, then join us at the table reserved for
our party.'

In depressed silence they did as he had bidden
them, letting the skirl of pipes, the almost hysterical
laughter of nearby dancers attempting to master the
intricacies of the Highland fling, wash over them as
they picked their way along the length of trestle
tables laden with dishes to satisfy every palate—
glazed Scotch salmon; smoked mackerel; scampi
cocktail; huge sides of roast beef; legs of pork with

stuffing and crispy crackling; turkey with prunes;
duckling with mandarins; sugar-glazed ham with
pineapple, and a bewildering selection of salads and
mayonnaises.

Claire refused all but a thin slice of ham, a let-
tuce leaf, and a small helping of tomato salad. She
was just about to turn away from the buffet when a
suave voice chastised:

'A good hostess must pretend an appetite if she's
not to make her guests appear greedy!' Plucking
the plate from her nerveless fingers, Rolf Ramsey
spun her round until she was once more facing the
buffet. 'Let's try again, shall we?' He slanted her a
wicked look. 'Together we'll satisfy our hunger.'

Claire ignored the outrageous innuendo. She
looked anxiously around for Jonathan and, seeing
him a mere pace away, grabbed him like a shield
for protection.

'J-Jonathan,' she stumbled, terribly conscious of
the twinkle in Rolf Ramsey's eyes, the slightly jeer-
ing smile curling his lip. 'You haven't met Mr Ramsey.' Then, with her attention fastened firmly on her
plate, 'Mr Ramsey, meet Jonathan Heywood, my
fiancé.'

She placed only the slightest stress on the word,
yet like an arrow aimed at the heart it landed
straight on target. Only she was aware of his jerk of
surprise, only she was able to compare the stilted
chilliness of his tone with its previous teasing
warmth. Whatever his background, she admitted
grudgingly, breeding showed in the manner in
which he acknowledged the introduction.

'My pleasure, Mr Heywood.' He inclined his head, but as Jonathan was struggling with a couple of plates, did not proffer his hand. 'I had intended to call at your office tomorrow,' he continued lightly, once more in complete control, 'to discuss various items of business that are still outstanding. However, if it's not convenient perhaps you could name another day?'

'Tomorrow will be fine.' Jonathan's face changed suddenly from ashen white to fiery red.

'Good! Then shall we join the others?'

The modicum of satisfaction Claire had gained from the encounter disappeared completely when, in spite of her efforts to prevent it, Rolf Ramsey managed to annex the seat next to her at the table. She was nervous of his close proximity, of the sloe-dark eyes sending startling messages whenever she was foolish enough or careless enough to allow her eyes to wander higher than the cleft in his very determined chin.

Charity, however, was a great help. Intoxicated by the success of the evening, and delighted by Rolf Ramsey's arrival, she monopolised his attention completely, leaving him little opportunity to torment the pale, dignified girl sitting quietly by his side.

Because not to have done so would have caused comment, she managed by degrees to swallow the small amount of food on her plate, listening without interest to the conversation ebbing and flowing across the table.

Aunt Effie was airing her favourite subject, the derivations of names. 'Take, for instance, my brother's name. Garff is a derivation of the Scandinavian "Grafir" whose origin means "valley of the waterfall".'

'Claire ...' When Rolf Ramsey spoke her name she looked up to meet the challenge of his mocking derision. 'To a Frenchman that means "clear". Claire Foxdale—Clear Running Water! Many Indian girls have similar names, because it's the custom for a mother to name her child after the first thing she particularly notices after childbirth. Did you know that, *ma petite*?'

To the others, his remark could not have seemed in the least offensive, yet it jabbed within her a raw, hidden nerve. For the first time in her life she experienced fierce anger, anger with Jonathan for showing a deference to this intruder that was almost obsequiousness; anger with Charity and her aunt Effie for making no secret of the fact that they found him charming, and anger with her father who was beaming approval upon this man who thought money could buy him anything, whose eyes, when they fell upon her, seemed to be staking out a claim, who wore his thin veneer of civilisation like a coat of clear varnish—showing signs of savagery underneath. The man who with a few lightly spoken words has reduced her to the level of an uncultured girl.

Pride showed clearly in her face when abruptly she rose to her feet to stare imperiously down at him.

'No, Mr Ramsey, I did not know. But when I think of it, your own name gives credence to the tale. Rolf—derived from "Hrofulf" the Old German name for *wolf*! I've heard it said that if a pregnant woman receives a sudden shock her child will be born showing some relevant mark or characteristic, which is why I find it very easy to believe that some time during your family's history a pregnant Ramsey female was frightened by some such animal!'

CHAPTER THREE

CLAIRE allowed her mare to pick its own way down a steeply-descending bridle path that led through a belt of trees, then levelled out into a heather-carpeted glen that was isolated, silent except for a river gushing and frothing over boulders that over the years had crashed down from the surrounding mountainsides and for ravens screeching a warning to any feathered interloper that dared venture too close to their nesting sites.

This was her escape hole, the secret retreat which supplied solace and accommodated her needs—a soft bed of fern on which to relax taut limbs and to disperse without trace tension-ridding tears; a void of silence into which she could pour out her fears without danger of hearing them repeated; the song of the river that had many times soothed her into relaxed sleep, and the towering backcloth of mountains whose permanent solidarity acted as a reminder that human troubles and fears were transitory.

She dismounted, allowed the mare to wander to the river's edge to drink, then flung herself down on to a cushion of fern, resting her head upon her outstretched arm, determined not to weep. Life, since Rolf Ramsey's arrival on the island a week ago, had become intolerable. Claire knew she had deserved to be reprimanded for the insult she had hurled upon his head on the night of the ball, but as familiar as she was with her father's moods, she had never imagined him capable of such cold, intense fury.

'You will apologise abjectly to Ramsey!' he had hissed, 'as I've already been forced to do. How could you, how *dared* you humiliate me so! Since childhood, you've been tutored so that when the time came for you to fill the gap left by your mother, to act as hostess in my household, there would be no danger of your embarrassing me by committing some unimaginable social gaffe. Up until this evening,' he had charged, 'I had felt able to congratulate myself that I'd achieved my aim, that the many hours I'd spent on your social training has resulted in perfection. *Perfection!*' He had thrown up his arms in a gesture signifying that words alone were not sufficient to register the extent of his disgust. 'The whole island must now be aware that my daughter possesses the manners of a guttersnipe!'

Claire stirred restlessly among the ferns, shying from the memory of the effort it had cost her to remain coolly unrepentant in the face of such criticism. Even Aunt Effie, usually the most understanding of creatures, had registered shocked disbelief, as had Jonathan and Duncan MacLeod. Only Charity had not conformed. In retrospect, her expression of triumphant delight was extremely puzzling. But regretful though she was about the upset caused to each of them, their reactions impinged as mere gnat bites compared with the attitude adopted by the one who had born without rancour the full biting lash of her tongue, the attitude that was responsible for her presence in the glen, driven into hiding by the man who for seven nerve-racking days had stalked her every movement, who had appeared at every function she had attended and remained like the shadow of Nemesis close to her side, who was impervious to snubs, impossible to ignore, and who had threatened to shatter her manner of cool disdain with penetrating looks and outrageous whispered advances that had sent fiery colour rushing to her cheeks.

'If he must behave like a rutting stag,' she moaned, rolling over to bury her face in cool fern, 'why, oh, why did he have to pick upon me as a likely mate?'

'Do you mind if I join you, *chérie*?'

She went very still. Only one man of her acquaintance possessed the impudent effrontery to intrude into secret places, only one man sprinkled his remarks to her with endearments learnt at the knee of a French-Canadian mother!

She rolled on to her back, staring dazed hatred into the face laughing down at her. 'You approach as silently as a snake through grass,' she choked. 'No doubt you were taught the art by your Indian brothers?'

He grinned, white teeth dazzling against the deep tan of his skin, then levered himself down, stretching lithe limbs alongside of her. Ignoring her taunt, he propped himself up on one elbow, so close she gasped, feeling smothered by the threat of his dominance.

'Why did you follow me? Are you so insensitive that you can't respect a person's wish to be alone?'

'So that you might retire into your cocoon?' he mocked softly. 'You seek solitude only because you're afraid of life—or rather of the glimpse. of life that I've given you—because up until now you haven't lived, merely existed, like the statue of a Madonna waiting to have life breathed into her, waiting for kisses to soften lips of marble, for a man's passion to send blood singing through petrified veins. But to experience deep emotion one must be prepared to experience pain, and it's that that you run from, little coward, the pain of ecstasy, the threat of almost unbearable joy! It's my belief,' he reached out a lean brown finger to stab an errant curl, 'that the only affection you've ever known is the lukewarm feeling you share with Jonathan, a man as devoid of spirit as a neutered tomcat. Marriage to him would be a tragedy, your life would be lived in a state of wedded virginity and at the end of it you would be mailed back to your Maker, a pathetic little parcel labelled: "Unopened. Return to Sender".'

Involuntarily she jerked away from a savage bluntness that would have been considered intolerable in any civilised society, hating more than ever the man who did not hesitate to strip her naked of modesty, to violate her tender dreams of a happy, companionable marriage by crudely introducing the subject of sex which, on the few occasions she had given it a thought, had presented an appealing picture of Jonathan as a gentle, considerate lover wooing her into shy submission.

'How dare you lecture me on love when all you

understand is lust!' she choked, barely able to mumble the words. 'Your prime aim is to satisfy your own selfish needs, therefore I won't waste my time trying to explain that giving and taking is the balancing act of marriage, acceptance of one another's differences is an essential ingredient of a good relationship.'

He forced her round to face him, willing her to meet his eyes. 'The differences between yourself and Jonathan are too great and too varied, *chérie*. If you won't think of yourself, then think of him. An unfulfilled woman can never make a happy, loving wife —your own complex, sensitive nature can only be delved by a man of unusual perception.'

'And you see yourself playing such a role?' She forced a peal of incredulous laughter. 'Your conceit is equalled only by your crude insensitivity!'

Her heart leapt to meet the sudden dangerous flare that ignited the depth of fathomless eyes. 'Must I prove to you how well I understand you?' His head hovered so close she felt the coolness of his breath against her cheek. 'Must I demonstrate how easily your pulses leap to life beneath my hands, how your mouth quivers at the threat of being kissed, how easily your eyes darken to the grey of an unfathomable sea in which a man could thresh against a tide of sanity, then drown in an undertow of passion? Why are you trembling, *mon ange*?' His lips landed delicately as a moth against the corner of her mouth. 'As yet, I've barely touched you? Nevertheless, I sense your clamouring to be taken. Deny, if you can, my lovely valkyrie,' he laughed down tenderly into wide, stricken eyes, 'that at this very moment you're ready and willing to let down your hair.'

'I can and do deny that such a wish is uppermost in my mind,' the words, forced through set lips, held a quiet intensity he had to believe, 'on the contrary, I find myself wishing that I *were* one of the maidens of Valhalla, because I can think of nothing that would give me greater pleasure than to hold the point of a sword at your throat!'

'Aren't you forgetting, my lovely,' though his teasing expression had fled his tone remained light 'that the maidens who rushed into the mêlée of battle to select those destined to death were motivated not by vengeance but by desire, they wanted hand-picked heroes with whom they could spend eternity in joy and feasting and making love. I would feel flattered to be chosen as your hero, to have you wait on me and fulfil my every wish for all eternity.'

Claire jumped to her feet, quivering with confusion and a weak desire to weep. With fists clenched hard, she dismissed him, imitating the hauteur her father used with devastating effect.

'Why don't you go home, Rolf Ramsey! Go back to your northwoods, your grizzly bears, and to the simple-minded friends who presumably appreciate your humour. We Manx,' she charged defiantly, tilting a proud chin, 'being of a highly sophisticated culture, look for qualities of diplomacy, sensitivity and consideration from our friends, which is why you could never fit into our society. It's a pity,' she dared a patronising smile, 'that when your family emigrated from these shores they didn't possess a determination to uphold the morals they'd been taught in order that they might act as an example to the less fortunate inhabitants of their adopted land. Your own manners and behaviour are proof that what actually did happen was quite the reverse— that the Ramseys opted to go native!'

He had risen to his feet and was standing in the classic pose of the Indian male—legs astride, arms folded across his chest, face impassive. Claire suppressed a quiver of trepidation, wondering what form of revenge he would choose to inflict, but then was completely deflated by the slow-widening grin that preceded his shout of laughter.

'Why, you unspeakable little snob!'

When his hands descended upon her shoulders she cringed inwardly, yet managed to retain her defiant look in the face of threatened retribution. His response was sharp, decisive and very much to the point.

'When I leave this island, *ma petite*, which may not be for some time yet, you will leave with me— as my wife! Don't fight the inevitable, Claire,' he shook her slightly, unmoved by her gasp of outrage. 'I want you, and I always get what I want. Not even the wariest of game can outwit the experienced hunter who studies the habits and nature of his prey so closely he knows exactly how it will react even before the trap is sprung!'

She rode like a fury out of the glen, away from the man who had made no effort to detain her, the man full of frightening assurance who seemed determined to unsettle her calm, uneventful exist-

ence. 'But he can't!' she consoled herself, frantic-
ally urging her mare through a belt of trees, head-
ing for the sanity of home. 'He's corrupted by
wealth, intoxicated by a power to influence, but
there's no possible way that he can impose his will
upon me!'

She saw two cars parked in the driveway as she
cantered up to the house, Jonathan's Rover and her
aunt Effie's battered Mini. She rode past them towards the stables and took her time unsaddling the
mare, brushing her down, then leaving her comfortably installed with a bag full of oats before making her way inside the house.

She was surprised to find her aunt sitting alone,
drinking coffee at a table set out on a sunny patio.
She looked up at Claire's approach, but her smile
seemed forced, her brow wrinkled with worry.

'Where's Jonathan?' Claire dropped into a chair
beside her. 'I saw his car parked in the drive.'

Her aunt opened her mouth to speak, then hesitated when the sound of raised voices penetrated the
open window of Garff Foxdale's study. The words
were indistinct, but the tone of anger was unmistak-
able.

'What's wrong?' Claire questioned sharply.
'Surely Jonathan and Father aren't *quarrelling*?'

The idea was unthinkable; she had never known
Jonathan to waste energy on argument and it was
quite out of character for her father to forsake
dignity to the extent of raising his voice to anyone.

'I'm afraid they must be.' Her aunt's hand shook
as carefully she set her cup back into its saucer. 'I

do wish they'd stop it, they've been at it for almost half an hour.'

'But why—what could possibly have gone wrong?' Claire gasped, feeling a strong premonition of disaster. She jumped when a door was banged shut with such force the noise reverberated through the house. When she heard her father's footsteps hastening across the hall she ran inside just in time to see his stiff-backed frame disappear from the top of the stairs and into his bedroom.

Twirling on her heel, she raced into the study and found Jonathan slumped dejectedly in a chair supporting his bowed head between shaking hands. Overwhelmed by a wave of maternal pity, she rushed to kneel at his feet.

'Jonathan dear,' she coaxed, 'you mustn't allow Father to upset you so. I know his fury can be devastating, but it's fatal to back down and allow him to suspect you feel defeated. It's so like him,' her voice rose indignantly, 'to create a major incident out of a small difference of opinion—that's all it was, wasn't it,' her voice sharpened, 'a storm in a teacup?'

She was shocked when Jonathan raised his head to show a face haggard with despair. Unable to meet her look, he dropped his eyes to the floor, then after a long, silent struggle finally managed to whisper.

'I wish it were a minor incident, Claire, but it's not, it's a major catastrophe! According to your father I've brought shame and ruin upon myself and my family, and also, because of our relationship, upon his too. I came to him seeking sympathy and advice,' he ejected a mirthless laugh, 'only to discover that your father is a hard, intolerant man. If the worst should come to the worst and I'm sent to stand trial I hope to God he's not the judge presiding!'

He was so completely downcast, so drowned in misery, she knew that she would need to be firm if she were to get any sense out of him.

'Stand up, Jonathan!' She rose to her feet, setting him an example. 'Stop wallowing in self-pity and tell me plainly and coherently what's happened.'

Mistaking the asperity in her tone for contempt, he flashed a quick look of hurt, but then to her great relief he stumbled to his feet, shrugged his shoulders erect, and began addressing a spot somewhere above her head.

'I've had a bad run of luck at the Casino,' he jerked, 'and lost quite a lot of money—some of which didn't belong to me ...'

She could have berated him, as she had done once or twice in the past, for his inability to resist the lure of the gambling tables, but it was not the time for recriminations.

'How——' she began.

'I borrowed it from a client,' he interrupted.

'Then all you need do is pay him back,' she pointed out, bewildered.

'It was borrowed from his estate without his knowledge.'

'*Embezzlement ...!*'

'No, dammit,' he burst out. Showing his first sign of spirit, he dropped his eyes from the ceiling to glare. 'Your mind runs upon exactly the same lines as your father's—I did not embezzle the money, I merely borrowed it intending to pay it back the moment I was in funds, but my client appeared on the island unexpectedly and arrived at my office demanding to see the books before I'd had a chance to redress the balance.'

Even before she asked, she knew with chilling certainty what his reply to her question would be.

'Wh-what's the name of your client?'

Cold fingers were squeezing her heart long before he ejected bitterly, 'Rolf Ramsey—a man reputed to be a multi-millionaire, who can afford to buy a derelict farm for which he has no use, fill it with costly relics, and pay a caretaker handsomely for doing next to nothing, yet who intends to sue me, to ruin my career, my reputation, and possibly,' anxiously he searched her face, 'even my marriage, all for the sake of a trifling sum that means less than nothing to him!'

CHAPTER FOUR

'FATHER, couldn't you lend Jonathan the money he borrowed?'

'Stole!' he corrected tersely, without lifting his head from his newspaper.

Claire had bided her time, planned an especially good dinner and had waited to introduce the subject until her father was settled in his favourite chair with a cup of coffee and a glass of brandy near to hand. At such times he was usually at his most receptive, but the moment she had mentioned Jonathan's name his relaxed mouth had adopted a grim, forbidding line.

'I think you're being very dogmatic,' she chided gently, 'nevertheless, if that's how you choose to view his unfortunate lapse it doesn't alter the fact that he is your future son-in-law and that a small act of charity could avert a major scandal.'

She felt hopeful when he lowered the newspaper on to his knee to give her his full attention. She swallowed hard, determined not to be intimidated by his cold stare.

'Am I hearing aright?' She jumped when the question scythed from his mouth. 'Do you seriously believe I would countenance a thief and embezzler as a son-in-law? Are you so lacking in family pride that you can contemplate marriage to such a man?'

'You speak of him as if he were a criminal,' she

defended hotly. 'You're biased against him, Father, you will allow no justification for his actions—already, in your eyes, he's been tried and sentenced!'

Garff Foxdale projected awesome authority when his judgment was challenged. Rising to his feet, he towered over her, resentful of being taken to task by his usually amenable daughter.

'You dare to accuse me of bias, of knowing only half the facts!' his voice trembled with barely restrained anger, 'whereas, in actual fact, I've followed my usual practice of collating, sifting, probing all the evidence available, and as a consequence I've been appalled by my findings! On only one count will I admit that my judgment has been at fault—my assessment of Jonathan Heywood's character was utterly and completely wrong!'

'Just because he borrowed a trifling sum of money?' To Claire, Jonathan suddenly appeared as a martyr, a whipping boy for her father's lacerated pride.

'Because I've discovered that he prefers gambling to working, and as a consequence an old-established, highly-respected business is on the verge of bankruptcy! And as for the money that was purloined,' he snorted, 'by anyone's standards, five thousand pounds is quite a hefty amount!'

'Five thou ...' Her eyes widened with dismay. 'Father, did you say *five*?'

But her father had stridden angrily out of the room.

After a fraught hour of stunned conjecture, Claire reached a painful decision. That Jonathan had erred could not be disputed, but the punishment hanging over him owed most of its weight to her own involvement. If he had been merely a casual acquaintance her father would have shrugged off his lapse as a youthful misdemeanour, and if Rolf Ramsey did not see him as an obstacle that was preventing him from possessing something he coveted he would not be half so determined to sue. Both of Jonathan's accusers meant to see him ruined; each one had a vested interest that was inextricably bound up with herself.

'I want you!' Rolf Ramsey's words echoed in her ears, *'and I always get what I want!'*

She went thoughtfully up to her bedroom to study the contents of her wardrobe, despising her motives, yet conscious that an appealing look would help to achieve success. Rolf Ramsey had an eye for beauty. Often she had noticed how his attention was held by the sight of shapely ankles, a voluptuous figure, or a seductive walk. He had made no secret of the fact that he considered her own attractions far superior to most—his weakness could become her strength, a strength she intended to exercise on Jonathan's behalf.

An hour later, when she arrived at his hotel and asked to be conducted up to his suite, she felt confident that she was looking her best. Her dress of leaf-green silk had been chosen deliberately in the hope that he might be softened by a reminder of the environment he preferred—cool green forests where breeze rustled softly through virgin leaves. Frivolous sandals, mere strips of kid and high spiked heels, were guaranteed to draw his appreciative eye to dainty feet and slender ankles. And then there was

her master-stroke, an exercise in psychology of which she felt inordinately proud, the way in which she had unpinned her hair, fashioned it into a single plait and tossed it casually across her shoulder in the fashion favoured by Indian beauties.
beauties.

Nervously she waited to be announced, then stepped with calm dignity into the sitting-room of his suite. He was seated at a desk studying a sheaf of papers, his tousled hair, casual shirt unbuttoned to the waist, evidence that he had not been expecting visitors.

Yet he did not look surprised when he rose to greet her.

'*Beauté du diable!*' Her heart soared in triumph. He had a tendency to lapse into his mother tongue whenever he felt deeply moved. 'You're so beautiful I can hardly trust myself to be alone with you!'

When he moved closer with a grace that was almost feline, triumph gave way to panic. Too late, she realised the danger of bearding a beast in his den, of putting herself at the mercy of dark predatory eyes that were transmitting signals she dared not try to interpret, holding her mesmerised by a gaze so intense and prolonged she felt involved in the deepest intimacy. In spite of herself she blushed, and felt transparent as glass when he gave a deep-throated chuckle.

'Come, sit down.' Taking pity on her, he took her by the hand and led her towards a couch. 'Tell me the reason for your most welcome but unexpected visit.'

Consoled by the thought that at least his mood

was as mellow as she had wished, she sat with hands clasped loosely in her lap and tried very hard to sound coolly reasonable.

'I've come—without my fiancé's knowledge—to plead for mercy, Mr Ramsey.' She felt proud of the even tenor of her tone, but became immediately disconcerted when with a swift wave of his hand he interrupted.

'Stop calling me Mr Ramsey—I shall refuse to listen to another word unless you call me Rolf.'

Sweeping down a curtain of thick lashes to hide quick resentment, she conceded, 'Very well ... Rolf.'

'Good!' He hooked an arm along the back of the couch, making no contact, yet instinctively she stiffened, feeling herself teetering on the brink of a yawning trap.

'Please take me seriously, Mr ... Rolf,' she pleaded in a nervous rush. 'I came here after long, serious thought, to ask you to overlook Jonathan's ... er ... lapse. I promise you that every effort will be made to repay the money that's owing to you. He's abjectly sorry and determined never to be tempted into such foolishness ever again, so what possible satisfaction could you get from allowing the scandal to break? I assure you,' her voice lowered to a whisper, 'that I intend to marry Jonathan whether you ruin him or not.'

'Don't scar your too-tender conscience with the thought that you've in any way influenced my decision to bring Heywood to justice,' he rapped.

She blinked, finding it hard to equate his previously unruffled manner, his teasing drawl, with a voice that sounded full of venomous intent. Wide-eyed, she stared at a profile that looked carved from stone, at flint-hard eyes, and lips set straight and un-yielding as steel.

'You and I share one common belief, Claire, and that is that traits of character are passed down from generation to generation. The first Ramsey to leave these shores did so with his pride shattered, his pockets empty, and bearing a burden of disgrace that would have shattered the spirit of many a lesser man, and all because of his dealings with a lawyer—an ancestor of Heywood's who founded the family firm—who hid his crookedness behind a cloak of respectability and who managed, with the aid of influential friends, to brand Angus Ramsey a bankrupt and a liar! To have a grudge is to have a purpose in life—I inherited Angus Ramsey's grudge, together with a determination to see him revenged!'

'I don't understand,' Claire breathed, wondering, as she stared wide-eyed, how she could have been misled by the quick smile, the lazy drawl, the easy manner he had used as a cloak to hide a core of iron. 'You were thousands of miles away, so how could you possibly have known what Jonathan was up to?'

'You're right, I couldn't,' he answered grimly, 'but I played a hunch and it paid off. I singled out Heywood to take the responsibility of purchasing the farm together with a large amount of equip-ment, put at his disposal an unlimited amount of money, then sat back and waited to see what would happen. He didn't disappoint me,' she shuddered

from a smile that was almost a snarl. 'Given sufficient rope, our friend Heywood very obligingly
hanged himself!'

She felt sickened to the very soul by the coldly
calculated exploitation of a man's weakness. What a
fool she had been to expect mercy from the descendant of a voyageur who had found pleasure in
battling against vicious elements, pitting his wits
against animals that roamed the forests, and who
had gloried in dominating mortals weaker than
himself.

'You're despicable!' she croaked. 'Utterly lacking
in compassion, incapable of decent feelings!'

His arm whipped down, trapping her around the
waist. Immediately her head snapped upwards,
eyes stormy, but abusive words faded from her lips
when she saw that once more his face had been
transformed by the lazy smile, the glint of devil-
ment she had come to know so well.

'I have feelings for you, *ma chérie*—Clear Running Water—but I doubt if you would consider
them decent.' Lifting her heavy plait of hair, he
twisted it around his neck, dragging her head so
close their lips were almost touching. 'There's one
way that you can save your weak kitten from drowning,' he crushed the words roughly against her
mouth. 'Marry me, Claire, and I promise that Heywood will be erased completely from both our
minds!'

'Never!' she choked. 'I refuse to be blackmailed
into become your *wife!*'

She was released so swiftly there was barely time
to breathe a sigh of relief before she saw him strid-

ing halfway across the room.

'Take time to think about it,' he tossed across his shoulder. 'Tonight I'm dining at a house near to your home—I'll call in while passing for your final answer!'

She had no need to consider the impudent proposition, Claire told herself a hundred times as she made her way home, rushed up to her bedroom and flung herself into a chair where for hours she sat gazing fixedly at the hands of a clock moving, inevitable as fate, towards the hour of Rolf Ramsey's arrival.

'If only there was someone I could talk to!' she fretted, mentally ticking off and dismissing her few acquaintances. Her aunt was too much in awe of her brother to side against him, and Charity MacLeod, whose honest, forthright opinion she would have valued, was so biased in favour of Rolf Ramsey she would no doubt congratulate Claire on her good fortune at having found favour in his eyes. She heaved a heartfelt sigh. She blamed her isolated upbringing for the fact that friendship had passed her by; she had learnt to accept and to live with the knowledge that she would never know the pleasure of sharing joys, hopes, and fears with another human being, and had built around her sensitive soul a shell of cool aloofness into which she could creep to recover from the pain of rejection and to hide from the world the knowledge that far from her being poised, assured and completely self-contained, too much solitude had resulted in a paralysing shyness.

It was a relief to be forced to change and dress

for dinner. Mechanically, she showered, brushed and coiled her hair into its usual elegant coronet, then chose a starkly simple dress, dark brown as her mood. As listlessly she made her way downstairs her spirits lightened at the sound of a car drawing up outside. Suspecting that it might be Jonathan, she ran to open the door, then stepped back in dismay when without a word of greeting he strode past her into the hall.

Ashen-faced, looking half demented, he croaked:

'The situation is getting desperate, Claire!' His mouth was working, his features distorted by a nervous twitch, his pale blue eyes, usually so placid, held a glistening, panic-stricken stare.

'Come into the study,' she urged quietly, holding out her hand. 'Father has a dinner engagement, he won't be back for hours yet.'

Like a grateful child he clung to her hand, drawing eagerly upon her strength. Pushing him gently into a chair, she left him for a moment to pour out a large measure of brandy, then returned to push the glass into his shaking hands.

'Drink this,' she coaxed, 'it will help you to pull yourself together.'

His teeth chattered against the rim of the glass when he took his first sip, but after he had tossed back the remainder slight colour crept back into his cheeks, his mouth gained a little of its composure.

Claire's heart felt ready to burst with pity as she sat down next to him and captured his hands in a comforting clasp.

'Now tell me what's happened?' she soothed, keeping her tone purposely light.

'You're a great girl, Claire!' he said huskily, his look of gratitude reminding her for a second of a devoted spaniel. 'I'm the luckiest chap in the world to have someone like you, loyal, dependable, steady as a rock in an emergency. I need you, Claire,' his voice reached hysterical heights, 'promise you'll never let me down!'

It took all of fifteen minutes' calm, reassuring talk before he became sufficiently coherent to jerk out:

'Two police detectives came to my office this morning—they questioned, they probed, politely of course, but with an insistence that brought home to me exactly what's in store. I never dreamt it would come to this!' To her horror he began to sob with a quiet hopelessness that underlined the depths of his despair. 'I was so certain that something would turn up to prevent disaster, but all my friends have deserted me, nobody wants to become involved, and Ramsey seems determined to hound me out of existence. Couldn't you speak to him, Claire?' The wretchedness of his appeal wrenched her heart. 'I've noticed the way he eyes you up—there's a chance, just a chance, that he might listen to you.'

'I already have.' The admission was breathed, barely audible, yet he seized upon her words.

'You have? What did he say?'

'He said,' she trembled a laugh, trying to sound contemptuously unconcerned in order to allay his justifiable anger, 'that he would drop all proceedings against you if I agreed to marry him!'

She braced, expecting an outburst of outraged derision, but was shocked when she saw a look of hope spreading across his features.

'What was your reply, Claire?'

The fact that he should even need to ask such a question caused the pain of a dagger being driven deep into her heart. When she continued staring dumbly, her eyes pools of hurt bewilderment, he jumped to his feet and grated.

'For God's sake, Claire! You hold my sanity in your hands, *tell me, what was your reply?*'

Stonily, feeling no one would ever be able to hurt her quite so much again, she mouthed, 'Don't worry, Jonathan, your sanity is safe. I've decided to marry Rolf Ramsey.'

CHAPTER FIVE

IT was many years since the elaborate headdress fashioned from beaten silver had been put to its original use. This morning it had been unearthed from the vaults of a bank and delivered to the house in good time for the ceremony.

Claire's father had been delighted when she had opted for a traditional Nordic wedding and had immediately ordered that the silver crown, an essential ornament of the wedding regalia, should be polished in readiness to enhance the beauty of the bride. It was at that moment resting on the top of Claire's dressing table, but she spared its glistening glory barely a glance as, woodenly, she began dressing for the ceremony, due to take place in less than an hour, that was to make her Rolf Ramsey's wife.

Charity MacLeod, who should have returned to Canada long since but had insisted upon remaining for the wedding, burst into the room after a tentative rap upon the door. She was overwhelmed with pride at having been allowed to help with the arrangements, yet not so blinded that she had failed to recognise weeks ago that Claire possessed none of the radiance expected of a happy bride. She had shrugged off her fancies, telling herself that the girl, being of such a complex and withdrawn nature, could not be judged as an ordinary mortal.

Only someone very close—as close as a lover—would be allowed to delve into what she suspected were very considerable depths.

To look subdued was one thing, but as Charity stepped inside the room she glimpsed, for one unguarded second, a look on Claire's face that could only be described as stricken.

'My dear, aren't you feeling well?' Charity darted forward, full of compassion.

'I'm perfectly well, thank you.' Claire shrugged her shoulders erect and forced her stiff lips to smile.

Luckily, Charity's attention was diverted, her fascinated eyes held, drinking in every detail of the outfit designed centuries ago for the brides of men, muscled and sinewed and clad in tough leather, who had pillaged and raped for pleasure and who had descended upon the island looking, in their twin-horned helmets, like reincarnations of the devil.

Claire eyed her reflection in a full-length mirror, congratulating herself that she had followed tradition to the letter, thinking how appropriate it was that she should be wearing black for her marriage to that devil Ramsey.

'My dear,' Charity stammered, once she had managed to overcome her initial surprise, 'your outfit is ... er ... startling. And certainly very original!'

She spun round from the mirror to allow Charity to examine more closely the outfit she had chosen, not out of sentiment, but because she could not have borne to carry out the pretence of marriage wearing white satin and a puritanical veil. The marriage was to be no more than a farce, therefore the theatrical costume would help her to keep her fears in perspective.

Charity's breath caught in her throat when she felt the full impact of a lovely young bride dressed all in black—black velvet that enveloped her slender limbs from neck to toe, from shoulder to wrist. A flower-embroidered, ribbon-trimmed bodice helped detract a little from the severity, as did a large jewelled medallion hanging from a heavy gold chain that reached to below her waist. But solemnity was again reinforced by a neck ruff of white pleated cotton and a coif of the same material that framed her face like petals fringing the heart of a flower.

Charity felt overawed, stunned, then just a little bit doubtful. 'My dear,' she began uneasily, 'Rolf is very much a man of today, no doubt he appreciates tradition as much as we all do, provided,' she hesitated, 'he doesn't have to become personally involved.'

When Claire's eyebrows rose in pretended puzzlement, she stumbled on, 'What I'm really trying to say is, I know it's absolutely taboo for the bridegroom to see the bride's outfit before the day of the wedding, but I've gathered from Rolf's conversation that he's expecting to see his bride wearing white, so won't your appearance come as a terrific shock?'

Her feelings of unease were not in the least placated when, looking suspiciously gratified, Claire smiled sweetly and cooed:

'Oh, I do hope not. That *would* be a terrible shame...!'

Aunt Effie's bustling entry into the room precluded further probing on Charity's part.

'My dear,' her aunt clasped her hands together in a furor of happy anticipation, 'the whole island seems to have turned out for the wedding! How clever of you to have planned an authentic Nordic ceremony during this, our Millenium Year! The visitors are absolutely agog. Now,' she crossed to the dressing table, 'let me help you on with your crown! Isn't it fortunate,' she beamed at Charity, 'that my brother never felt tempted to dispose of this heirloom? In the old days, it was every girl's ambition to wear the traditional silver crown, but of course many of them had to make do with a fillet of myrtle or tinsel. However, the crown of chastity, as it was then known, was considered to be so important that it became common practice to keep a silver crown at the church to be lent to girls who were too poor to provide a coronet of their own. There!' Having placed the crown to her satisfaction she stepped back to admire her handiwork and to appeal to Chastity, 'Doesn't she look simply superb?'

In spite of her misgivings Charity had to agree that Claire's waxen cheeks and cloud-grey eyes framed inside a pristine coif had been lent a haunting fragility by the contrasting depth of dramatic velvet that was hugging her curves so closely every movement brought a reminder of supple, feline grace. Apropos nothing she could name, she felt a sudden surge of sympathy on Rolf's behalf, wondering at his nerve in aspiring to marriage with a girl who carried her magnificent garb with such dignity and who wore her silver crown with all the panache of an imperious queen.

'Oh, isn't it romantic!' Aunt Effie twittered, quite carried away. 'I do love recreating the past, don't you, Mrs MacLeod? I'm just a little bit disappointed that we're not to emulate the form of marriage by capture, the old Nordic custom of a would-be bridegroom capturing his bride at the very door of the church as she was about to be married to another.'

When a deathly silence fell she became aware, in spite of her excitement, that she had committed a dreadful *faux pas*. Colour rose in her cheeks as, keeping her eyes averted from Claire's expressionless face, she mumbled, 'Forgive me, my dear—I'll go and tell your father you're ready.'

The doubts Charity had been harbouring were immediately confirmed. Concern for Rolf sharpened her tone as she demanded of Claire, 'Will Jonathan be attending the wedding?'

'I certainly hope so.' Coolly, Claire put her firmly in her place. 'On such an occasion one needs the support of one's oldest and dearest friend.'

The one concession that had been made to present-day comfort was the car that carried Claire, her father, and her aunt to the tiny parish church built of stone, with low walls, a much-weathered roof and a turret from which was issuing a frantic peal of bells. It had no grandeur, no architectural pretensions, but was merely a plain, spotlessly white, rectangular building with a black roof of Manx slate, the usual east window and west doors.

Claire had been christened at its small stone font,

had worshipped there since childhood and because she drew from its atmosphere an inner strength she had insisted, in spite of her father's strong arguments that it was too small to accommodate the expected number of guests, that she would consider no other church, even if it meant that the best part of the congregation had to remain outside. But it soon became evident from the number of cheering, waving people lining the route to the church that no existing place of worship on the island would have been spacious enough to contain the cram of sight-seers that fell into stunned silence, then erupted into an appreciative roar when Claire stepped with the aplomb of a leading lady out of the car.

Solely with the aim of discomfiting her unsuspecting bridegroom, Claire had arranged for the Nordic ceremony to take place out of doors on a raised dais, a wicked piece of guile which no doubt accounted for the thunderous frown she glimpsed on his face as uneasily he waited—as a bit actor awaits his cue —beneath the porch at the entrance to the church. Fiercely glad that she had managed to plead prettily and successfully with her father that the New-World Canadian would strongly oppose any personal involvement in archaic customs, and that the success of the pageant depended solely upon his remaining ignorant of procedure, she approached the church, walking between her father and her aunt, each holding her by an arm, pulling her forward as she enacted the signs of reluctance once considered essential of a shy Nordic bride.

Attired in a black cut-away coat, grey waistcoat, and pinstriped trousers, her bridegroom seemed uncertain how to react when she approached him. She had hoped to make him appear incongruous, but she had to acknowledge that she had not completely succeeded. Undoubtedly, anger was simmering beneath the surface, but outwardly he looked calm, dignified, and quite extraordinarily handsome.

She was dragged passed him, still simulating reluctance, and set down upon a ceremonial chair. Six girls chosen from a nearby village moved forward to hold over her head a canopy of shawls to keep her protected from evils, then her father placed upon her feet shoes which tradition decreed had to have neither buckle, strap, button, nor other fastening if she were to hope for easy delivery in childbirth. He then placed a silver coin in the right shoe and her aunt a gold one in the left, to ensure her future prosperity.

Betraying an expression that was markedly cynical, Rolf Ramsey moved forward when instructed, to be joined with her in pagan matrimony by a Viking 'priest' whose muttered, unintelligible words gave rise within her to an hysterical urge to giggle. All during the ceremony she looked for a sign of awkwardness or embarrassment, but her bridegroom carried out his duties with dignified aplomb, reacting so promptly to his cues that it was impossible to guess he had not had the benefit of even one rehearsal. When a lighted candle was pushed towards her, signalling the culmination of the ceremony, she passed her hand lightly over the flame, symbolising that she was cleansed of any evil influence that might still have been clinging

to her from her former life, then she rose to her feet
and felt tempted to sweep a curtsey when, with a
burst of applause, their audience showed its appreciation. But the temptation subsided when, after a
quick sideways glance, she read resentment in her
bridegroom's rigid jaw. Elated by this confirmation that her plan to humiliate him, to make him
feel a complete outsider, was succeeding, she in-
dudged in a smile of triumph as side by side they
walked into the church where a minister was waiting to proceed with the legal marriage ceremony.
But triumph faded with the echo of her first foot-
step against the stone-paved floor.

The interior of the church was dim; an organ
was softly playing and as a choir of children began
to sing she shivered, chilled by a blast of cool
solemnity.

'*I take thee ... to my wedded husband ... to have
and to hold ... from this day forward ...*'

It could *not* be her voice making those meaningless promises to this stranger standing so stiffly erect
by her side, the lean planes of his face made to
look even more alien by flickering shadows cast
from candles set in sconces that were imitating the
spears that had served a dual purpose during the
days when marriage by capture was common, mas-
querading as candleholders during the ceremony,
but available for defence in case of attack.

'*To love and to cherish ... till death us do
part ...*'

Her bridegroom's voice held no trace of the
negligent drawl she had come to associate with him.
He sounded as darkly earnest as he looked when he

slid a heavy gold ring on to the third finger of her left hand, the finger from which the *vena amoris*, the vein of love, was purported to run straight to the heart. She did not lift her head to return his light kiss, but remained with eyes downcast, fighting an astonishing feeling of shame at having cheated him of a memory cherished by most men— that of seeing his bride dressed in virginal white walking down the aisle to meet him.

Outside the church they ran the gauntlet of showers of rice, then the moment she had been dreading arrived, they were alone together for the first time, being driven back to her home where the reception was to be held.

But whether because the anger she sensed within him ran too deep for words, or because he was conscious that their widely-grinning driver was watching them closely through the interior mirror, he stifled his resentment until they entered the silent hallway of her home. Taking advantage of their few minutes' start on the race of pursuing guests, he grabbed her shoulder and stared without speaking for long, fraught seconds.

'If you were hoping to confound me by wearing black for our wedding,' he finally grated, 'a colour chosen by both sinners and penitents, then you've certainly succeeded! What sort of woman are you, Claire?' Contemptuously he eyed her, showing equal dislike of black velvet and snow-white coif. 'I'm finding it hard to decide whether I've married a chorus girl or a nun!'

The wedding breakfast was typically Nordic and enormous. Laid out on tables, waiting to be served, was fish of every description, fresh, cured and smoked—shoals of salted herring swimming in seas of onion and vinegar marinade; filleted mackerel smothered in tomato sauce; crisp fishballs; huge platters of reindeer and mutton salamis; a variety of smoked and cured meats; mountains of boiled eggs and dozens of individual cheeses made by farmers whose herds grazed high in mountain meadows. Bowls of wild mountain berries gathered early that morning and flown specially to the island were placed with accompanying jugs of sour cream to be poured over the fruit, then sprinkled with coarse sugar. Waffles were carried hot from the kitchen to be spread with butter and blueberry jam or, as an alternative, plates of nutty crispbreads that brought out superbly flavours that owed their excellence to the clear sea and sparkling mountain air of the region from which the dishes had originated.

Trays holding glasses filled with liberal measures of brandy and *aquavit* began circulating the moment all the wedding guests were assembled. Twirling the stem of a glass filled with the potent schnapps between quivering fingers, Claire seized the first available opportunity to make her escape from the side of her thoughtful, unfamiliarly morose bridegroom, edging cautiously towards the fringe of the nearest group of people, so that her disappearance into the crowd was made to seem entirely accidental.

'My dear, I've never witnessed a more dramatic marriage ceremony ...' 'Such an unusual wedding ...' 'How serene you looked, darling, not a

hint of stage-fright, in spite of the size of your audience ...' Somehow, she managed to murmur all the correct replies, schooling her expression into lines of tranquillity so that no one would guess how much she was regretting the trick she had played upon Rolf Ramsey, the man whose chosen environment was the northwoods whose inhabitants, though basically tamed, had inherited the ability to emulate the wary, knowing creatures of the wild, whose sharp eyes and keener scent enabled them quickly to detect an unfriendly presence.

As if fate had decreed that it should happen, she turned away from one group of people, meaning to progress to another, and found herself face to face with Jonathan. They had exchanged no words, had had no contact of any kind since the night Claire had decided to accept Rolf Ramsey's proposal, but as they stood together, isolated in a crowd, eyes locked, she could not muster so much as one word.

Jonathan, however, had plenty to say. 'Claire, why have you been avoiding me?' His hoarse mutter was pitched low enough to reach only her ears. Careful, as always, not to be seen to offend against society, he kept his expression light, his mouth tightly smiling, as he continued to rebuke, 'I thought better of you, Claire, but like everyone else on the island you seem determined to see me ostracised. Although Ramsey kept his word and the scandal did not break, rumours have been spreading, and the fact that I'm no longer welcome at your father's house is adding fuel to the gossips' bonfire. I still love you, my darling, and I feel certain that even though you ditched me in favour of Ramsey

you must still have a soft spot for me, which is why
I dare to plead with you to prove the gossips
wrong, to demonstrate that you're prepared to be
friendly so that others might follow suit!'

She stared, her grey eyes wide with astonishment,
wondering how she could have overlooked his shal-
lowness of depth. Incredibly, he had managed to
convince himself that he had been jilted and was
being unjustifiably condemned! Yet she could feel
no anger, merely sad compassion for the man whom
she had once, after all, been prepared to marry.

On impulse, she linked her arm through the
crook of his elbow and smiled encouragement; if a
gesture was all that was needed to put his world to
rights it would be mean of her to withhold her support.

She heard his gasp of relief, felt gratitude in the
grasp of his fingers upon her hand and tried not to
appear too apprehensive at the sight of every dark
head when Jonathan began parading her around
the room.

She sensed the astonishment of guests confronted
by a bride strolling arm in arm with the man she
had supposedly jilted, cringed inwardly from the
upraised eyebrows and the trail of scandalised
whispers left in their wake as they passed group
after chatting group.

It seemed an age, yet could only have been
minutes before her feeling of apprehension was
justified when from behind them a voice addressed
Jonathan in an extremely pronounced drawl. 'I'm
afraid, Heywood, that I must ask you to relinquish
your claim upon my wife.' His tone was light, his

expression suavely polite, but she was not deceived —only she felt the impact of eyes with depths darkly glowering. 'It appears,' he held out his hand towards her, 'that the time has come for the proposing of toasts.' Miraculously, the crowd had melted out of their vicinity, leaving them stranded within an arena of antipathy. For the benefit of many watchful eyes, they had to act out the charade of friendly civility, yet Claire felt as vulnerable as an innocent thrown to the lions when, confident that he could not be overheard, her husband challenged in a savage undertone:

'What would your toast be, I wonder, Heywood? Victory to the vanquished?' He slid a possessive arm around Claire's shoulders, giving an outward impression of a proud, devoted husband. 'Sorry to disappoint you,' though he continued to address Jonathan his eyes did not leave her face, 'but my country, young though it is, possesses traditions of its own, standards that have been handed down from men who were among the first to brave the wild, lonely wilderness, pitting their wits against the untamed and the untameable. One of them is that it is absolutely taboo to poach on another man's territory, or to filch game from another trapper's snare. The punishment meted out to any man who transgressed was swift and terrible and might still be, Heywood,' he turned on Jonathan to menace slowly and with bloodcurdling intensity, 'right now in the present day!'

CHAPTER SIX

WITH a great show of pride, Garff Foxdale proposed a *skai*. 'To my daughter Claire, and my son-in-law Rolf, may great happiness be heaped upon their marriage!'

'To Claire and Rolf!' With appropriate solemnity, glasses of *aquavit* were raised to the level of the third waistcoat button, guests bowed, their eyes meeting, the drink was quaffed, glasses lowered to their previous level, again with eyes meeting, then after a second bow the glasses were returned to the table.

Very conscious that her bridegroom's tolerance was wearing thin, Claire sipped her way nervously through innumerable toasts wishing that the prolonged reception would come to an end so that she could lay her throbbing head on a comfortable pillow.

'By the way,' her aunt piped up, 'where are you spending your honeymoon?'

Claire's hand jerked so suddenly some of the liquid spilled out of her glass. Stupidly, her mind had been so preoccupied with arrangements for the wedding she had given no thought to what came after.

'That's my secret.' Rolf came to her rescue as, fiery-cheeked, she sought for a convincing answer.

'You mean that even Claire doesn't know?' her aunt probed.

With an inscrutable smile he parried, 'One blade of grass looks pretty much the same as another to lovers.' He stroked a glance across Claire's features, mocking her swift rise of colour. 'Wouldn't you agree, *ma chérie*?' he insisted wickedly.

Pinned by the interested eyes of her inquisitive aunt, she stammered agreement and felt almost grateful to him when, sweeping an arm around her waist, he urged her forward.

'Please excuse us,' he requested her aunt, 'your brother is beckoning us rather urgently.'

She sensed that the restraint he had been exercising for so long was beginning to grow irksome as he wove a way through guests who were showing signs of boisterousness as, well fortified with spirits, they hailed the appearance of musicians and began a concerted surge towards a doorway leading into a room whose floor had been cleared for dancing.

'How soon before we can take our final curtain call?' Rolf hissed sarcastically, abandoning all pretence of urbanity. 'If I'd known I was to be involved in a charade, set upon a stage to pull faces and entertain an audience like some dancing puppet, I would have insisted upon an elopement!'

'You underestimate your talents.' Claire's smile was full of sweet acidity. 'There's one role in particular in which you excel—you have, after all, managed to convince most people that you're civilised!'

She slipped out of his hold, managing just in time to evade the grip of fingers intent upon inflicting bruising chastisement upon her waist, and hastened to gain protection at her father's side.

'Everything is ready,' he beamed upon his mystified son-in-law, 'it's time for Claire to dance off her crown.'

She did not dare so much as a sideways glance as her father escorted them both into the ballroom where all the guests had been segregated, the women at one end of the room and the men at the other. Knowing exactly what to expect, she made no effort to resist when a crowd of girls descended to blindfold her and to push her into a circle made up of every unmarried girl in the room. Holding her crown in one hand, she began groping for the nearest girl who, once caught, would be entitled to wear the silver crown, as superstition decreed that she would be the next to follow Claire's example and get married. Amid much shouting and laughter, she managed without difficulty to pin down a victim who then took her place in the centre of the circle and proceeded with the dance that went on and on until every maiden had been crowned.

She chanced a look to the far end of the room where her bridegroom was undergoing a ceremony that was meant to be similar but which, because of their high spirits and the amount of *aquavit* downed by the young men involved, had predictably developed into a minor brawl. She was just in time to see him being tossed into the air, then descend, swiftly disappearing beneath a scrum of broad shoulders.

For the first time in weeks she laughed aloud with genuine pleasure, thoroughly enjoying the thought of his discomfiture, but her laughter turned into a gasp when without warning she was lifted from her feet and carried in strong outstretched arms above the heads of wildly cheering guests.

With the ease of an athlete Rolf transported her upstairs and into her bedroom where she was dumped unceremoniously on to the bed. Tousle-haired, aggravated, yet with barely quickened breath, he commanded:

'We're getting the hell out of here! I'll give you five minutes to change into something sensible, and if you're not ready when I get back I'll perform a fertility rite of my own that has a guaranteed, one hundred per cent rate of success!'

Her suitcases had been packed earlier and stored in the trunk of the car. Her going-away outfit, a suit of lightweight cream wool woven especially for her by the islanders, looked as forlorn as she felt when she unhooked it from the rail of a cavernous wardrobe. With shaking hands she slipped into it, keeping one eye on the clock, ever mindful of the forcible promise made by Rolf Ramsey. He had not spoken lightly, but more in the manner of a man whose patience had suddenly snapped. He had coped better than she had expected with a day that to him must have been full of shocks and surprises; it said much for his ability to adapt to circumstances that, mostly, an indulgent smile had played around his lips, his attitude of easy-going tolerance had remained unruffled. But now he was angry and did not care who knew it—it was as if the kitten she had been teasing had suddenly developed into a growling jungle cat!

Her bedroom door burst open just as she was zipping up her skirt.

'Good! I'm pleased to see that you've acted upon my advice.' He strode soft-footed into the centre of the room, dark, lean, his profile as godlike as the ones primeval Indians had chipped out of sheer granite walls—all sharp, all edge.

As he eyed her she waited, complacent that he could find no fault with her impeccable appearance. But his irritable comment came as a shock.

'Don't you ever wear bright colours? Must you always be so conscious of your dignity—can't you relax, shriek, yell, or even indulge in a very feminine weep?'

Rapidly, she blinked, determined that he would never know how nearly he had shocked her into displaying just such a sign of weakness.

Pinching her chin between thumb and forefinger, he raised her head high and peered suspiciously down. Aloof grey eyes returned his stare, patrician nostrils flared slightly, her mouth pursed prim with disdain. He grinned, half admiringly, when she refused to back down to his challenge.

'Inside, all fire and guts—outside, a Nordic ice queen,' he drawled. 'Which qualities did Heywood find most attractive, I wonder?' His lips curled into a snarl. 'My guess is that he leant upon your strength, enjoyed the protection of your attitude of command, your imposing hauteur, your condescending manner. Did he feel safe and pampered under your wing?' His dark head swooped until his lips were hovering a fraction away from her distressed mouth. '*I* don't intend to worship you from afar, *ma chérie*, to play consort to your queen. I'm

your husband—a parched hungry human—and I
want a warm, eager wife in my bed!'

He plundered her mouth with a roughness she
found terrifying. Desperately she willed her body
to stay calm, not to respond by so much as a flicker
of an eyelash, but when he pulled her deeper into
arms coiled tightly as a snake, every nerve end reacted with rapture to the lean, supple threat of his
powerful body.

'*Mon ange*,' he murmured hoarsely, '*mon ange
blond*...Look at me, let me see into the depths
of your honest grey eyes when you tell me that you
love me!'

Though her heart was pounding, roaring like a
fireball, her mind a whirl of confused thought,
Claire slowly allowed her lashes to lift until they
lay in a thick golden fringe around eyes turbulent
as a storm-tossed sea. As he held her, staring long
and deeply, his smile faded and two parallel fur-
rows of displeasure appeared on his brow.

'Why the frown?' she asked, panting as if she
had been running a race. 'Don't you like what you
see? Surely you weren't foolish enough to believe
that because you'd bartered and paid for your bride
in the manner of your Indian friends, I should will-
ingly adapt to the role of a quiet, submissive wife,
prepared to walk two paces behind you for the rest
of my life? Look hard, Rolf Ramsey, if you want to
see the truth! I hate you! I despise you! Your touch
fills me with revulsion! My disgust at the way you
treated Jonathan—roasting his nerves on a spit of
anxiety—will remain with me for ever! If it's a

wife you want, then go back to the northwoods where you belong and take your choice of the many women I'm sure you'll find available!'

When his white teeth snapped, ready to interrupt, she trembled out the accusation, 'Don't pretend to be outraged—Charity told me about Angus Ramsey and his Indian wife, the woman from whom you've no doubt inherited your very basic ways!'

His hands dropped to his sides and as he stepped away from her she shivered, feeling stripped by eyes staring ferociously out of a face totem-grim. 'So *that* is the reason why you're afraid of me!' He stood with arms folded tightly across his chest as if curbing an impulse to shake her violently. 'Your virgin flesh creeps from my touch because I'm too basic, too much of an animal to appeal to a puritanical nun! It's time you grew up, Claire,' the grating timbre of his voice made her jump, 'time to face the ultimate separation from a dominating parent who has taught you every social grace but deprived you of the sensuality that is the right of every beautiful woman. You sense in me the beast that's in every man—I can't deny that it exists— but only time will convince you that I'm not a sadistic brute.'

'Time...?' Her head jerked upward to cast him a look of hauteur. 'You mean you intend to impose your presence upon me even though I've made my aversion plain?'

She felt pleased, sensed she had scored a point when a muscle jerked violently in his cheek, but her smile froze when with a cat-like bound he closed the gap between them. Thonged-leather fingers bit into the soft flesh of her arms as, quietly murderous, he hissed, 'You're my wife, today we were joined together in matrimony, and whether you like it or not, together we're going to work at our marriage to make it as good as can possibly be managed!'

Schooled to obedience by the threat of being dragged forcibly from the house before the eyes of scandalised guests, Claire allowed him to lead her downstairs, across the deserted hallway, then slid without protest into the passenger seat of the car that was standing in the driveway ready to transport them to the airport. A couple of times she felt tempted to escape his loose grip upon her arm and run pleading to her father, but was prevented by the certainty of what his reaction would be. In her father's eyes, Rolf Ramsey had assumed every virtue desirable in a son-in-law, not the least being the fact that his roots were buried deep upon the island. *'Manx must marry Manx!'* he often reiterated, complacent in the knowledge that his own family's pedigree had remained pure. If she were to try to explain he would become patronising, simply refuse to believe that to her sloe-eyed, hawk-faced husband she was no more than a prize that he had won, a piece of barter that he would not hesitate to discard the moment some other girl took his fancy.

The atmosphere inside the car was pregnant, filled with a heavy pulsating throb that had nothing to do with the sound of its racing engine. They drove some miles in silence, then Claire felt driven into breaking the unbearable tension with a quavered question.

'What time does our flight leave? I suppose we're going to Canada?'

'That was my intention,' he agreed coolly, then surprised her, 'but I've change my mind.'

He did not elaborate, seemingly preoccupied with his task of negotiating safely the many curves and blind corners that made the quiet, hedge-lined roads hazardous to unwary drivers. They passed through many small parishes, each with its own tiny church and surrounding graveyard where incised crosses leant drunkenly, and ancient moss-covered headstones had inscriptions written in the ancient Manx language.

When the car breasted a steep hill, she recognised immediately the panorama of sea, sky and heatherland that was typical of the southern end of the island. Suspicion became confirmed when through the gathering dusk she glimpsed the lights of houses lining streets mounting upwards from a small harbour. Beyond, she knew, lay nothing but an isolated stretch of gorse and heather that rolled on and on until it tumbled over the edge of massive cliffs that were home to colonies of razorbill, puffin, and guillemot.

Unnerved by his silence and the prospect beckoning, she questioned sharply, 'Where are we going? This isn't the way to the airport.'

'Why are you sounding so panic-stricken?' he drawled. 'Is the thought of solitude so appalling? Lovers are supposed to seek it, or didn't you know that, *ma chérie*?' When she treated his observation with contemptuous silence, he continued, slightly regretful, 'I'd planned—had looked forward—to introducing you to my wilderness. I wanted to watch the amazement on your face when you saw for the first time a mere segment of the northwoods looming as an infinity of trees, sombre, brooding, almost overpowering in their majesty. We would have journeyed into the interior to see massive outcrops of granite—portions of the earth's crust so old it dates back to an era that ended some six hundred million years ago—rocks that form sudden steep precipices, sharp ledges, odd, ungainly shapes that are beautified by splashes of red and green lichen. And then there's the water ...' She shifted in her seat, puzzled by the dreamy overtone that had developed in his voice as he recalled treasured memories for his own benefit. It was almost as if he had forgotten her very existence.

'... what an inadequate word to describe such a varied abundance of gently flowing, tumbling, cascading magnificence! And to stun your mind further, there's the impact everyone feels at their first sight of centuries-old trees towering healthy and strong, though the bases of their trunks show the ravages of a fire that erupted over a hundred years ago.'

Feeling a surprising eagerness to see for herself the sights that were imprinted so indelibly upon his mind, she uttered with involuntary pleasure, 'It sounds wonderful—I should love to go there!'

He deserted his memories of the northwoods to flash her a derisory look, then confused her with the cryptic observation, 'Perhaps you will, one day, but not until you're ready to really appreciate it. At the moment your vision is not clear enough, your sympathies are not sufficiently attuned. These are problems of immaturity that will resolve themselves once you dare to stretch your foot to the full length of your blanket.'

Feeling affronted, Claire would have lapsed into a sulky silence were it not that such an action would have helped to confirm Rolf's insinuation that she had not yet grown up. She was saved the effort of speech, however, when the outline of a cottage loomed out of the deserted dusk. She guessed his intention immediately he braked and slowed the car to a standstill on the footworn path that ran past the cottage, squat and sturdy as the landscape, with walls built of thick local stone set in clay mortar that seemed sugar-iced with layer after layer of whitewash that had been applied regularly year after year.

Its quaintness was emphasised by a roof of straw thatch held down by herring net and ropes tied horizontally to projecting stone pegs in the gable walls then interwoven by others slung over the ridge, forming a secure network that reminded Claire of a granny wearing an ancient hairnet.

As she clambered from the car she braced, mustering defiance of his next, obvious, suggestion.

'Shall we go inside?' He did not disappoint her.

'Why . . .?' Her chin tilted. 'The interior will come as no surprise to me, it's a typical early-Manx cottage,' she patronised, airing her knowledge, 'a survival of an ancient Celtic type of farm settlement. A few families—half a dozen or so—would each build a cottage, forming what's known in the West Highlands as a *clachan*, and between them would work scattered acres of corn plots and rough grazing. Some of the men supplemented their meagre income by fishing, quarrying flagstones and lintels from the cliffs, weaving, cobbling, doing smithy work, anything, in fact, that brought in a few extra coppers. They lived in a world of their own, all speaking only our mother tongue, Manx Gaelic, and never mixing with others outside of their own tightly-knit community. This cottage is probably the only one surviving of the last of the *clachan*.'

'Thank you for the résumé of my family history,' Rolf tossed laconically over his shoulder as he turned an ancient key in a well-oiled lock. When the small black-painted door swung open he ducked his head and proceeded inside without inviting her to follow. As she stood teetering on the step there was a glimmer of light that slowly developed into a warm golden glow that suffused the interior of the cottage, eventually reaching far enough to spill over the step.

'Welcome to Balla Ramsey!' He approached her, watchful, narrow-eyed. 'Shall I carry you across the threshold?'

Without waiting for her reaction, he scooped her into his arms, kicked shut the door, and carried her into the middle of the room.

'*Put me down!*' Claire pounded angry fists against the wall of his chest. 'You still haven't answered my question—why have you brought me here?'

When, grim-faced, he set her down upon the stone floor she shivered, imagining she could feel the chill of stone seeping into her very bones. His dark eyes were sombre as he towered over her, the oil lamp behind him casting an eerie, elongated shadow across stark, whitewashed walls. He spoke without emotion, yet to her over-sensitive ears his voice seemed to echo with the vengeance of spirits long departed.

'By your choice of wedding ceremony you demonstrated plainly your preference for living in the past. But you were playing, Claire, as a child plays at dressing up in her mother's clothes, which is the reason I decided that it's high time you began facing up to reality. Here, at Balla Ramsey,' he waved an encompassing hand, 'you can indulge to the hilt your thirst after nostalgia by learning to cope with life as it was lived over a century ago when deprivation bit iron into men's souls and bonny young brides were turned into aged hags before they reached thirty! Nevertheless, those women remained loyal loving wives to the men they married —does that help to supply an answer to your question, Claire, are you now beginning to understand what lesson you've been brought here to learn...?'

CHAPTER SEVEN

CLAIRE stared fixedly at the fly-blown dial of a grandfather clock so ancient it seemed to have become over the years an integral part of the wall. Its steady ticking thudded into a mind so stunned it was struggling to suppress wild notions that she might be losing her sanity, or that the cheerless, poverty-stricken cottage filled with antiquated jumble might be the setting for some unspeakable nightmare.

Her eyes slewed from the dresser filling almost the width and height of one wall, its shelves packed with lustre jugs, rosy basins, and a complete willow-patterned dinner service, towards the open hearth that took up the whole of the gable-end wall of the cottage. A pile of burnt-out ashes lay on the worn hearth stone that was level with the floor. There was no grate of any kind, just a lugged iron cooking pot and kettle hanging by a long pot-chain fixed inside the throat of the chimney flue. A spinning wheel stood at the side of the hearth—was he really expecting her to use it, she wondered dully, to spin her own thread and knit him a gansey to wear when he went fishing?

Her eyes drifted upwards to the ceiling where the undersurface of *scraa*, long felt-like strips of top sod laid neatly from room ridge to wall top, was visible between the spaces of laddered roof beams.

There was no doubt in her mind that the arrogant Manx-Canadian had meant every word he had said. He was determined to see her humbled—she was equally determined that he would not! Her best defence, she decided, would be to adopt an attitude of mute defiance, to ignore his ridiculous edict and carefully avoid becoming involved in any argument.

He had turned away, giving her time to absorb his shock announcement. The spurt of a match drew her attention. He was squatting by the hearth, coaxing flame to ignite a pile of dried-up twigs and twisted paper. She heard him grunt satisfaction when the twigs caught alight, but was not quick enough to evade his look when he slewed round to face her.

'The place will look much more homely once the fire gets going,' he encouraged with a grin. 'There's a cupboard beneath the dresser full of provisions, why don't you have a forage,' he suggested casually, 'and see what you can rustle up for supper?'

Seizing upon the opportunity to demonstrate what she thought of him and his suggestion, Claire sauntered across to a hard wooden settle, sat down, then stared in front of her wearing an expression of disdainful hauteur.

Rolf was quick to decipher her message. She felt his eyes upon her face, thoughtfully probing, and caught the tail-end of a long, almost soundless whistle.

'So that is the way it is going to be—mute rebellion, eh, *ma chérie*? So be it!' he said crisply, turning back to his chore of tending the fire. 'If you don't work, you don't eat—we shall soon discover whether or not hunger can breed reform!'

He continued chatting, seeming unconcerned by her silence, while he tended the fire, directing a draught from ancient bellows until the peat was glowing red. 'You will soon develop the particular skills needed to turn out a meal without all the paraphernalia of a modern kitchen,' he assured her.

She could have told him that for the past few years her only connection with the kitchen had been the daily planning and discussion of menus with her father's very able housekeeper, but she resisted the temptation and stared fixedly ahead, trying not to listen.

She sensed that he was smiling when, crossing over to the dresser, he began rummaging among the surprising amount of provisions. 'I've been living here for the past two weeks,' he surprised her by saying. 'Hotel rooms invariably become irksome, so at the first convenient opportunity I moved in here and found it the next best thing to living out of doors. Getting down to basics offers a challenge I'm sure you'll enjoy, Claire, if you will give it half a chance.'

He actually sounded serious!

'There's a challenge in learning to use the skills and the imagination needed to cope with what some might term the "inconveniences" of primitive life.' He straightened, closed the door of the dresser with his foot, then crossed over to dump the items he had chosen on to the table. 'Why be stubborn?' he coaxed the back of her proud head. 'Why not decide, instead, to co-operate? One of the best ways I know for two people to develop a relationship is for them to work closely together in a situation where there are ample opportunities for giving and taking, sharing chores, discovering those things that give mutual enjoyment, and those that don't, indulging in pleasant conversation. Living close to nature presents an ideal opportunity to recognise one's faults and failings—in such a situation it should not be difficult for us to get to know each other—intimately.'

She stiffened, alarmed by the meaningful stress he had placed upon the word. She was not fooled by the slyly proffered olive branch; whether she co-operated or not the outcome would be the same. But if, as he had claimed, living rough was an aid to insight, then he would soon discover that she was not the type to give in without a fight!

She remained tensely alert when he lapsed into silence, knowing that he was willing her to respond and quite determined that she would not. She heard the crisp slicing of a knife as he worked at the table behind her, caught a pungent whiff of onion, and was reminded that she had eaten practically nothing throughout the long, traumatic day.

The kettle was simmering on the *slouree* and as he bent down to unhook it and to hang in its place the lugged iron cooking pot, firelight leapt along the planes of his face, sharpening his profile, deepening the hollows beneath his cheekbones, igniting his dark eyes with a leaping, saturnine glare. The pot sizzled when he tossed in a spoonful of dripping, followed seconds later by minced meat, then the thinly sliced onion. The aroma that rose from the pot was almost unbearably delicious.

Claire looked away, drooling, as he stirred, browning the ground meat and onion in the hot dripping, but her hungry eyes would not be thwarted and were drawn back to feast upon the can of mushroom soup, the milk, the pepper, then finally the noodles that Rolf tossed into the pan before he covered it with a lid and left it to simmer.

'Sorry I can't offer to switch on the television,' he apologised, dropping into a cushionless wooden rocking chair and stretching his feet in front of the fire. 'I could have brought a radio, I suppose,' he frowned, 'but to be honest, the thought never occurred to me. There are books and papers around somewhere,' he waved a vague hand. 'As you don't seem inclined to talk, perhaps I should look them out for you?'

'Please don't bother,' she refused frostily, driven almost to distraction by the delicious smell permeating the room. 'I'm feeling rather tired,' she snapped, 'is there somewhere in this hovel where I might try to get some sleep?'

'You know the layout of the cottage as well as I do,' he mocked. 'As they're all identical in construction you must be perfectly well aware that there's one bedroom only.'

'And a storage loft!' she flashed, then reddened when he grinned, conscious that she had been tricked into a neatly-laid trap.

'So there is!' he agreed lazily. 'A cramped piece of space beneath the roof where the crofters' children normally used to sleep. How fortunate for me,' he drawled, glancing the length of his outstretched legs, 'that we won't be needing to use it.'

Willing the trembling from her knees, Claire stood up to leave him, attributing to his remark the importance it deserved by ignoring it completely. 'Are you gentleman enough to fetch my suitcases from the car?' she requested stiffly, 'or must I get them myself?'

'Of course not.' With languid ease he heaved out of his chair. 'I'm prepared to make that small concession to ensure the comfort of my bride.'

Claire began to shiver the moment she entered the small dark room in which a plain deal chest and one rickety chair were dominated by a four-poster bed made up with coarse, homespun sheets and pillowcases yellowed with age, and a covering of heavy woollen bed quilts that had almost certainly been woven on a hand loom by some weaver in a previous century.

She slid out the top drawer of the wooden chest and shuddered from the sight of a calico nightdress, wondering about the woman who had spent many painstaking hours inserting tiny stitches along yards of seams; had hand-stitched buttonholes so meticulously that there was not the least sign of fraying even today, and speculating most of all on the thoughts she must have been entertaining when she had decided to edge the very functional collar with a strip of incongruously dainty lace.

'Deprivation of the body can be easily forgotten if the heart is rich in love!' Rolf spoke softly behind her, demonstrating an uncanny ability to read her mind.

She swung round, startled, and cannoned into him when he stepped into the restricted space be-

tween the chest and the bed. Dropping the suitcases to the floor, he shot out his hands to steady
her, then held on, staring through the gloom as if
he was finding it difficult to let her go.

She felt trapped inside a tomb. Not so many miles
away her very civilised father would still be entertaining their wedding guests; people would be ensconced in comfortable homes doing everyday,
mundane things such as filling a kettle from a tap,
then boiling it on a stove; pressing a switch to flood
a room with light; undressing in warm, heated bed-
rooms and padding barefoot across carpeted floor to
slide appreciatively into a comfortable bed. Such
reality seemed a thousand miles away as she stared
into the hatchet-carved face of the man she had been
insane enough to marry. Why had she done it? She
had felt bitterly hurt by Jonathan's betrayal, but
not heartbroken nor even, if she were truthful, terribly surprised. But she had imagined that he loved
her and the discovery that she had no one—that
there was not one person in the whole world that
she could really rely upon—had rendered her hope-
lessly uncaring of her future. But now the numb-
ness was wearing off, the awful reality of her folly
was beginning to register and the fear, the dismay,
the sheer blind panic, was written plainly on her
face as she stared up at him.

He expelled a hissing breath and released her,
stepping sharply away. 'Get undressed, Claire,' his
tone was expressionless, 'the bed is comfortable and
well aired, when you're ready I'll fetch you in some
supper.'

Her relief was tremendous, yet still her fingers

moved panic-swift as she fumbled her way out of her suit and into a nightdress, ruffled, silk-bowed, and diaphanous, a mere wisp of almond-pink gossamer that had been meant to be worn under very different conditions.

The sheets felt rough when she slid between them yet held no hint of chill, and the mattress filled with down and goosefeathers moulded her inside a warm cocoon so that when she snuggled deeper, heavy eyelids drooping, she felt a sensation of floating, borne on a thousand tiny wings. She had almost drifted into sleep when the door opened and Rolf walked into the room carrying a tray holding a bowl full of the stew he had concocted, a glass of milk and a guttering candle balanced inside a dull pewter holder.

Setting the candleholder on top of the chest, he approached with the tray, ordering gruffly, 'Sit up. Today you've eaten less than would fill a sparrow, you'll feel much better after this!'

The delicious smell rising from the bowl was too much to resist. Eagerly Claire slid upright, then remembering her near-nakedness she grabbed the top sheet and pulled it over her breasts, tucking one end under each arm.

'Bare is beautiful,' Rolf rebuked gravely. 'You possess a figure many women must envy, so why not show it off, glory in your good fortune? A woman who is inhibited about her body has usually been taught that nudity is immodest—a word that should be deleted from our language. Forget your father's old-fashioned teaching, *ma chérie*,' he slid the tray across her knees and sent her into a state of utter confusion by relaxing on to the edge of the bed, 'try to be completely honest with yourself, to shed the niceties and inhibitions of everyday life, then you'll begin to experience a truly ecstatic sense of freedom. I doubt your capacity for greed, *ma belle femme*, but I feel certain that once you've taken a first tentative bite you'll discover that you possess quite a healthy appetite.'

She blushed to the tips of her ears. They both knew that he was not talking about food. As he lifted a laden spoon to her lips, coaxing her to eat, his smile was provocative, his action symbolic of the serpent leading Eve into temptation.

'There,' he approved when she had swallowed the first delicious spoonful, 'that wasn't so bad, was it? If you relax your hold upon your sheet of armour,' his glance derided the offending bedsheet, 'you'll be able to feed yourself. But perhaps,' his soft laughter jeered, 'you like to have me ministering to your needs?'

The choice was a difficult one. He had no intention of leaving her alone, therefore she had either to relinquish her modesty or suffer the pangs of ravenous hunger which one spoonful of the stew had only served to aggravate. As she dithered, she wondered if there was any truth in the supposition that primitive tribes had the ability to extract tranquillising potions from everyday plants and herbs and, if so, whether Rolf was in possession of such knowledge, because just one spoonful of the stew had induced a beautiful euphoria within which she felt warm, contented and very much cared for—a likeable, un-usual sensation she felt loath to relinquish.

'Please stay ...' she mumbled, keeping tight hold of the sheet, her pleading eyes upon the dipping spoon.

He sighed. 'So beauty is not for sharing, eh? Very well, just this once I'm prepared to humour you.'

Claire felt satisfied long before the bowl was empty. When, heavy-eyed, she turned her head away and slid beneath the sheets, indicating that she had had enough, Rolf returned the bowl to the tray. The bed creaked when he stood up and with a murmur of satisfaction she burrowed deeper into her pillow, then winced when a fine hairpin jabbed her head. Thinking he had gone, she raised a languid hand to pluck the remaining pins from her golden coronet, then tensed rigid when a low-voiced request reached from directly overhead.

'Let me help you ...'

Condemning herself for her stupidity, she struggled upright, forgetful in her anger of the need to screen her near-nakedness from his glinting eyes. Fool that she was for being naïve enough to be lulled by false concern and a clever change of tactics into thinking that he would be content to leave her in peace!

'*I always get what I want ...!*'

The words hammered into her brain as she jerked erect, ready to storm, and found his lean brown face, his powerfully muscled body, much nearer than she had imagined.

'I can manage, thank you,' she choked, her torrent of furious words smothered to extinction by his suffocating shadow.

Predictably, he ignored her words. With the awkwardness of a man handling something fragile and precious, his fingers began probing through her silken hair, plucking out the fine pins and laying each one carefully aside. Denuded of their support, the heavy coils fell down around her shoulders, each strand tipped by a spiralling curl, pale and golden as her wedding ring.

'I'm sure that as a child you were taught never to retire without brushing your hair,' he murmured, burying his lips among the silken strands.

Feeling suddenly cold and very much afraid, she watched him reach for the hairbrush she had left on top of her suitcase and submitted in silence when with slow, tender strokes he began brushing her hair. She kept her head bowed, her eyes downcast, steeling herself to remain calm but becoming more and more conscious of strong fingers lingering against her throat, of his steady breathing and the rise and fall of his broad chest exposed by a shirt worn with a negligence he seemed to favour, unbuttoned to the waist and with sleeves rolled up above his elbows so that his pantherish movements were unrestricted. With a lock of hair tumbling rakishly on to his brow he looked the epitome of freedom, a man who lived by the doctrine he preached, a doctrine of uninhibited thought, word and deed, of healthy appetite and unrestrained passions.

Movement never lies! Suddenly Claire realised the meaning of the words once read and subconsciously retained. Although people might lie and deceive easily in speech and writing, their bodily movements reflected their true emotion. At that moment her bedroom seemed too small to contain the presence of a man who was generating all the strength and purpose of a forest prowler—a man who could cast off civilisation as easily as a snake casts off his slough!

Fingers of panic squeezed her throat when Rolf threw down the brush and clasped a hand upon each of her shoulders.

'Why did you marry me, Claire?' His voice was thick, rendered unrecognisable by deep emotion.

The fingers around her throat tightened, forcing out the terrified admission. 'Because you gave me no choice. What other reason could there be—I hardly know you!'

'That's irrelevant.' Slowly he drew her towards him.

'It must be relevant,' she tensed to resist his forceful pressure. 'Unless you imagine I could fall in love at first sight.'

'Why not?' he breathed, lowering over her as she gave up the struggle and dropped back panting upon her pillow, 'I did ...'

He captured her mouth with a kiss that was a stamp of ownership, a punishing reward for torment that drained every pocket of resistance, dragged response from every hidden part of her.

'*Je me consume pour toi, amour de ma vie!*' At times of strain man's strongest trait emerges; he was at that moment wholly Gallic, a dedicated, desirous, hot-blooded Frenchman.

Claire fought like a she-cat, spitting, writhing, clawing her way out of hands that seared her cool, virgin skin like a fiery torch; wrenched her mouth out of reach of lips murmuring words she did not want to hear; strained hard to escape the pressure of a body transmitting a virile plea for a passion to match his own, a passion that was driving him beyond the edge of sanity.

When he laughed deep in his throat and caught both of her wrists in a determined hand, she knew that the battle was almost lost. A pink wisp of chiffon mocked her from the floor where it had been contemptuously tossed. Her body, bared to his flame-flecked eyes, glistened slim and supple beneath a golden veil of hair that was clustered into damp tendrils on her brow and at the tender nape of her neck. Making one last desperate effort, she wrenched a hand free and struck, ripping four sharp fingernails down the length of his face.

His head jerked back into a pool of candlelight and in spite of her white-hot fury, she felt sick with dismay at the sight of blood oozing from scratches running in four straight lines from cheek to chin like some barbaric tattoo.

'Manx cat!' he growled, making no effort to stem the flow of blood.

'Savage Indian!' she spat, appalled by what she had done, yet aware that it would be fatal to show it.

When his hand shot out to grasp her neck she sensed that he had been driven too far, and for the first time she felt the cold, implacable fury that

Jonathan had experienced being directed towards herself.

'I can ignore your contempt on my own behalf,' he gritted through clenched teeth, 'but I resent deeply the attitude of people such as yourself who are intolerant of others simply because they're of a different colour, have different customs, language and religious beliefs. No race, not even that of the high and mighty Foxdales, can be superior to others at all times and in all places—although the Indians themselves are not faultless in this respect because they, too, consider themselves superior to most. They tell a story of the Great Spirit who formed the world and then its inhabitants. His first attempt at making man was a failure, since all he achieved was a "very imperfect and ill-tempered being"—the white man. Displeased with this result, the Great Spirit then resorted to black clay and made the black man. He was much better than the white man, but was still not perfect. So he then took a piece of pure red clay and formed the Indian, who was perfect in every respect.'

With cold, concentrated fury, he spelled out, 'Tolerance is vital if racial conflict is ever to diminish, remember that, Claire,' he threatened hardly, 'if ever again you feel tempted to denigrate a race of people whose women could teach you everything you need to know about the obligations a wife owes to her husband!'

Shamed by his loyalty towards friends whose race she had thoughtlessly used as an instrument of provocation, she croaked, 'I was forced into a legal marriage, but I will not be forced into a physical one!'

'No, Claire, you will not!' The sudden grating of his voice made her heart lurch. 'For if, by some miracle, you should develop into a warm and loving woman, I'll take you as a wife only if you come begging to me —on your knees!'

CHAPTER EIGHT

IDLY, Claire stirred a panful of porridge with a
large ladle fashioned out of horn. She had slept
surprisingly well and had awakened early to the
sound of hundreds of squawking seabirds and a
patch of sky hanging like a spotless blue curtain
across tiny, squared windowpanes. With difficulty
she had managed to push up the bottom half of the
window to sniff early morning air heavy with the
smell of seaweed and to listen to the suck and drag
of shingle far below at the bottom of the cliff, as the
sea carried out her daily chore of swilling and scour-
ing all manner of flotsam from the shore.

As the day promised to be warm, she had unearthed from her suitcase a pair of cotton slacks and
a navy-blue sleeveless top with a white anchor em-
broidered on one shoulder—which was perhaps
accountable for Rolf's dry observation when tentatively she had stepped out of her bedroom and into
the living-room.

'The sea is woman—implacable most when she
smiles serenely!' He straightened up from the fire
he had been tending. 'Come to think of it, I don't
think I've ever seen you smile. If ever I do, I shall
consider it not at all a bad beginning to our friendship.'

'If ever I do,' she replied, feeling much less composed than she looked, 'it will be because I consider

a smile the best way to end an unwanted relationship.'

Demonstrating his lack of both malice and conscience, Rolf had abandoned the subject to question with a grin. 'I feel like fish for breakfast, don't you? If you make a start on the porridge, I'll go out and see what I can catch.'

He had then sauntered out, giving her no time to argue, and she had waited until the sound of his cheerful whistling had faded into silence before reaching a decision and moving thoughtfully towards the dresser. He had left her with no option but to co-operate, or starve. She could have attempted an escape by trekking the few miles to the nearest road in the hope that one of the few motorists to penetrate this far south would offer her a lift home. But the thought of the gossip that would ensue when word spread, as it surely would, that a bride of mere hours had fled from her husband, offended her dignity, as did the thought of her father's displeasure, his stern, probing questions.

'*An experienced hunter studies the habits and nature of his prey so closely he knows exactly how it will react!*' The fact that Rolf Ramsey felt confident enough to leave her unguarded in the cottage was proof that already he found her as readable as an open book.

She rummaged in the cupboard and with great relief discovered a packet of instant porridge oats that required only the addition of water before cooking. With intense concentration she tipped a measured amount of oats and water into the heavy pan, stirred briskly, then heaved it up on to the *slouree* that was dangling over the open fire.

Sweat trickled between her shoulderblades as earnestly she stirred to prevent the mixture from sticking to the bottom of the pan. Outside, the air was balmy, not a hint of draught penetrated through the open doorway so that, as the peat glowed increasingly hotter and steam rose from the bubbling pan, the interior of the cottage grew uncomfortably warm and moisture trickled in rivulets down her face and neck, disappearing into the valley between her breasts. Deciding that the porridge was ready, she began struggling to lift the heavy pot from its hook. Heat seared her bare arms and shoulders as she leant across the fire, wrapped a protective cloth around the handle of the pan and positioned herself for the necessary mighty heave.

'Leave it ...!' The command rang out just as she was bracing to take the weight of the heavy pot.

Rolf crossed the floor in a couple of strides and with an ease she envied plucked the pot from its hook and set it down at the side of the hearth.

'It looks good.' His smile of approval had a puzzling effect upon her pulse rate. 'Can you milk a goat?'

'Of course I can't!' She flushed, feeling herself the butt of his wicked humour.

'In that case, I'd better show you how. Porridge without milk is an unappetising prospect.'

She realised that he was serious when he began edging her towards the door. 'But I couldn't ...' she flustered. 'I don't like goats ... they ... they smell!'

'But their milk tastes good,' he insisted firmly,

propelling her outside, 'and I need hardly point out that in this remote area we can't expect a milkman to call.'

As he led her past various outhouses chickens ran pecking between their feet, and in a field next to what once had been the smithy, Loghtan sheep were grazing, an ancient breed native to the island, with fleece the colour of dark Spanish snuff, the rams distinguished by their striking headdress of multiple curling horns.

The goat, tethered to a stake in one corner of the field, looked up to eye them belligerently as they approached.

'This is Margot,' Rolf introduced the goat, urging Claire forward with his hand beneath her elbow. 'Don't be timid, she's quite peaceable. Stay here awhile and make friends with her, I'll be back in a minute.'

Waiting until she was sure he was out of earshot, she leant forward, staying well out of range, to plead nervously, 'You *will* make allowances, won't you, Margot? You see, I've never milked a goat before—as you'll very soon find out—and normally I wouldn't dream of attempting to, but that devil Ramsey thinks I need to be humbled—which is why you're about to suffer the sort of discomfort that ought never to be inflicted upon a lady. So will you please co-operate? Help me to wipe that condescending smirk off his face?' Perhaps it was wishful thinking, but she felt sure Margot's beady eyes softened and one lid drooped downward in the manner of a conspiratorial wink.

Nevertheless, her confidence waned the moment

she saw Rolf striding back towards her, carrying a bucket, a cloth, and three-legged milking stool.

'I prefer to do the job without a stool, myself,' he told her cheerfully, 'but you'll probably manage better with this. However, you mustn't be disappointed if you experience difficulty at first; animals won't give milk as freely to a stranger as they will to someone to whom they've become accustomed. Now watch carefully,' he squatted between Margot's front and hind legs, then began gently rubbing her udder with a wet cloth before grasping a teat in each hand. 'Make the sides of the forefinger and thumb press upon the teat more strongly than the other fingers, use both hands at once, and press alternately but so quickly in succession that the alternate streams of milk sound like one continued stream. It must be done fast, to draw away the milk as quickly as possible, and you must continue as long as there's a drop of milk to bring away.' He straightened, placating the restless goat by patting her flank. 'Now you have a go!'

He positioned the milking stool precisely, then when Claire had slid nervously on to it, keeping a wary eye upon restive hooves, he placed a pail between her knees and guided her hands on to the teats, clasping his own hands around hers to demonstrate the technique he wished her to emulate.

She held her breath, almost overcome by Margot's pungent body odour, then experiencing an overwhelming urge to surprise him, she concentrated hard upon imitating his actions. When a steady stream of milk began hissing into the pail she almost fell off the stool with shock. Triumph such as she had never before known brought a glint of enthusiasm to her grey eyes and a tremulous upward curl to her mouth. By the time the last drop had been squeezed from the generous udder her back was breaking, her knees holding the bucket felt numb, yet there was a lightness in her step, a glow of satisfaction permeating her whole being, when Rolf retrieved the pail and helped her to her feet.

'Well done!' he applauded, sounding slightly surprised, then annoyed her by explaining away her success with the grinning observation, 'Margot must have sensed a shared affinity—both of you have natures that are extremely sensitive.'

Four speckled brown trout lay on the kitchen table where he had left them. Expertly, he gutted and cleaned the fish, dusted them with flour and salt, then laid them in a buttered skillet placed directly on top of glowing peat. After washing her hands in water drawn earlier that morning from an outside well, Claire ladled out the porridge, then, still feeling a glow of achievement, she set down upon the table a jug of fresh milk.

Reading her expression correctly, Rolf sat down opposite, wearing a wide grin. 'Later, I'll show you how to stuff and prepare a chicken and to make a sourdough starter.' She hesitated with the first spoonful of porridge halfway to her lips, to raise interrogative eyebrows. 'Sourdough bread,' he explained, 'was part of the staple diet of the pioneers who opened up the Canadian wilderness. In those days, nothing was measured, each man devised his own recipe as he went along, but whatever method was followed the result was invariably delicious. There is nothing, *ma chérie*, to compare with the taste of golden-brown hotcakes straight from the grill.'

'I'm sure you're right,' she agreed politely, becoming wary of his air of easy camaraderie, conscious that once again she was in danger of becoming disarmed by this hunter who used charm to bait his traps. Carefully she scraped the last of her porridge from its bowl before continuing. 'What a pity you were born too late to join the ranks of the voyageurs you admire so much. Doubtless you would have been in your element ensnaring creatures of the wild, slitting their bellies to strip the pelts from their backs.'

She had intended to sound sarcastic, scornful of barbarity, yet had not imagined that her words would have such an impact upon the man whose jaw went rigid, whose knuckles showed white as his fingers tightened around his spoon. She eyed him curiously, sensing that she had prodded a sensitive nerve. 'Well,' she insisted coldly, 'that was how the foundation of the Ramsey fortune was laid, wasn't it?'

Strangely, she gained no satisfaction from his wince but felt startled and a little ashamed when in a low-voiced monotone he admitted, 'Yes, it was. I'm far from proud of the part my family played in destroying the culture of a proud Indian race during the quest for more and more furs. The Crees were a nomadic people who lived the life of forest hunters until they made contact with the first of the fur traders who tempted them into the large-scale trapping of furs by bribing them with guns and by developing and exploiting their craving for alcohol.' His grim face darkened. 'Because of a growing demand for beaver hats from the fashionable public of Paris and London, and for coats and stoles to drape across the shoulders of rich, over-indulged women, a proud race was deprived of its culture and some species of animals were brought dangerously close to extinction. Fortunately, laws were passed to protect the animals, but help came too late to save the buffalo hunters, the dwellers in tepees, the great horsemen and archers, the tribes of courageous warriors.'

His tone was intense, his eyes sombre, yet dimly Claire recognised that she was seeing only the tip of the iceberg of scorn he felt for men who would stop at nothing to satisfy their greed for gold. Suddenly, it became easier to understand and forgive his harshness with Jonathan, his intolerance of his weakness. Feeling nervous of his silent brooding, yet at the same time encouraged by this glimpse of unsuspected sensitivity, she queried:

'I assume that you're no longer involved in the fur trade?'

'That branch of our business was sold off years ago,' he assured her quietly, 'and the proceeds were given to the Crees as a trifling recompense for all the harm they had suffered. And in return,' he surprised her by reverting with such suddenness to his habitual teasing that her heart lurched, 'I was made a blood brother, an honorary member of their tribe. During my initiation I was given this,' he plunged a hand inside his shirt and withdrew a blue clay medallion dangling on the end of a leather thong, its rim carved and scrolled, its raised centre-piece resembling an antlered stag. 'The blue elk,' he tapped it with a thumb nail, 'whose name I was given, and with whose virtues I was supposedly endowed.'

'And they are . . .?' she queried, faintly overawed.

'Bravery in battle,' he softly replied, daring her to drop her eyes, 'and in making love.'

Fiercely, she blushed, reminded of the scene she had tried all morning to forget, resenting the re-stirring of pulses only just subdued, the return of a deep inner ache that had suffused her body from the first moment it had felt his touch. She hated him for what he had done to her, for disrupting her life, for arousing deeply-buried emotions—for shar-ing those emotions then having strength enough to cast them aside. Perversely, she resented his re-jection more keenly than she had resented his attempted possession. But at least, she consoled her-self, she could now feel safe, for, if nothing else, Rolf Ramsey was a man of his word. He had vowed never again to force his physical attentions upon her, and somehow she was able to believe him utterly.

'I think,' she prevaricated, 'the fish are burning.'

'*Tiens!*' He jumped up to rescue the trout from the sizzling skillet and laid them, crisp and succul-ent, on to a serving plate. 'Eat up, *ma chérie*,' he confounded her. 'You will need all your strength if you are to survive the battle that is already rag-ing deep inside you.'

To her furious embarrassment a deepening blush

told him that this time it was he who had scored a hit on a sensitive target. She could have borne amusement, but felt unbearably transparent when gently he chided, 'Clear Running Water—how well the name suits you, *mon enfant*; being starved of love and affection has resulted in your becoming an emotional misfit in this permissive age. Obviously, you have been taught to believe that sex is a subject never to be talked about in polite society, thereby rendering an entirely natural and beautiful experience into a great taboo, never to be discussed nor even mentioned.' He leant across the table, his eyes darkly earnest. 'Loving need not always be serious, Claire. Sharing happiness, fulfilment and contentment can also be fun!'

She wanted to lash out, to punish him for exposing her mentally and physically to ridicule, and she did so, making full use of the only weapon she possessed.

'Of course I'm aware of that!' she blustered, her grey eyes turbulent. 'Jonathan and I often laughed and joked when we made love—but then he and I were so eminently suited, we liked the same things, were products of the same environment, shared the same principles and priorities. For selfish reasons of your own you spoiled all that, yet you have the effrontery to expect me to fall into your arms, to be prepared to make love to a man I hate, whose touch makes me cringe, whose mere presence causes me to shudder!'

'If you're attempting to annoy me by implying that you and Heywood were lovers then you can save your breath, because I refuse to believe it,' he told her with infuriating calmness. 'You were never in love with him nor he with you.'

'How can you even pretend to know?' she began, made furious by his perspicacity.

'Only when the well-being and happiness of another person becomes as important as one's own well-being and happiness can the state of love exist,' he patiently explained. 'So how can you explain away Heywood's meek acceptance—I would even go so far as to call it his relieved approval—of your decision to marry me? And how could you have made such a decision,' he argued steadily, 'unless some inner voice was making nonsense of your argument that I cause you to cringe and shudder, *insisting*, cowardly little liar, that what you claimed to feel was the very opposite of the truth!'

'I *do* hate you!' Claire stood up, quivering with rage. 'What hope can there be of us achieving a satisfactory marriage when we disagree every time we speak?'

Rolf's usually merry eyes were stern, his face implacable, when tersely he told her, 'A wildly passionate union would be ideal; unswerving devotion would be desirable, but in the absence of either we can still achieve a perfectly good marriage provided we have mutual tolerance, respect, and some moments of shared contentment. And as for our disagreements, these are inevitable between two people of such widely different interests, attitudes and backgrounds as ours. We each have our faults, Claire, so when conflicts arise we must learn to compromise—that way we will survive. I much prefer a marriage that is disrupted from time to time by argument to one that exists peaceably but on a basis of deceit.'

Suddenly Claire's overstretched nerves snapped. She wanted to scream, to rant and rave, to rip wide open the scratches of his face that were not yet healed.

'*You* want, *you* think, *you* know!' She stamped her feet and stormed. 'What about me? Am I to have no say at all in this mockery of a marriage?'

He did not rise to the bait, did not return fire with fire, but remained seated, his mouth curling upwards, the dawning of a twinkle in his eyes. 'Our marriage is a mockery only because you have made it so, *ma chérie*. Yet I am not despondent, because I see before me a woman slowly emerging from a cocoon of ice.' With shocking speed he jerked upright and appeared as if spirited to stand in front of her. Sunshine slanted through the open doorway so that her braided hair glittered like a crown as he took her chin between two fingers and tilted her head to study her furious profile.

'There is hope for us yet,' he breathed. 'You are angry, you are dishevelled, you smell ever so slightly of goat, yet never have I seen you looking more beautiful, more desirable, more warmly *human!*'

CHAPTER NINE

An uneasy truce had been declared. The day had passed in comparative harmony, each of them striving to be polite and co-operative as they shared the chores and maintained cool, casual conversation. But the ability to keep a discreet distance vanished as inevitably as the sun vanished below the horizon. As they entered the cottage, closing the door against encroaching dusk, Rolf lit the lamp so that a warm pool of light flooded across the table and fell on to the floor, lapping the edges of heavy furniture ranged around shadow-shrouded walls.

Claire shivered, imagining ghostly shapes lurking in dark corners. Rolf was quick to react. Mistaking her shiver for a sign of chill, he climbed up the ladder leading to the loft where he had spent the previous night and returned carrying a roll-necked sweater, one of the thick-knit woollen ganseys worn by fishermen to protect them from raw, biting winds.

'Here, put this on!' He tossed it towards her. 'Sit down by the fire while I fix supper.'

She dared not refuse. It was useless pretending that an eruption was not pending; the very air around them seemed to crackle a warning whenever they came close, even though she had striven all day to ensure that they made no physical contact, had edged sideways to manoeuvre past him in confined spaces, shrinking as if from a leper.

She shrugged into the heavy sweater and felt immediately comforted by a weight of warmth and a faintly oily smell. With a sigh of contentment she curled up in the rocking chair at the side of the fire and watched Rolf positioning spare ribs, cooked earlier that day, on to a makeshift barbecue that he had fashioned out of wire. He was amazingly capable; already he had constructed a refrigerator by filling a wooden crate with perishables and anchoring it with rocks to the shady bed of a nearby stream. But the feat she most appreciated was the shower he had contrived by punching holes in the bottom of a large plastic container unearthed from the trunk of the car, stopping the holes with golf tees tied to a string and hooked over the handle of the container so that they would not get lost, then hanging it, filled with water, from the branch of a tree, controlling the force of the water by pulling out the desired number of tees. A sheet of plastic, again filched from the car, provided a curtain of privacy —a refinement she suspected he would have cheerfully done without but one for which she was enormously grateful.

Lulled by the rhythmic motion of the rocking chair and by the heat of the fire-warmed gansey, she nodded off, and was startled awake by Rolf pushing a plateful of barbecued spare ribs and baked potatoes beneath her nose.

'Come along, sleeping beauty,' he teased, 'wrap yourself around these!'

It was a long time since she had tasted anything

more delicious than the ribs she held in her fingers and gnawed ravenously, concentrating like a small, hungry animal until every sliver of meat had been cleared from the bones. She then turned her attention upon the potatoes, scooping out the floury, perfectly cooked, centres oozing with butter, then scraping up every morsel leaving the inside of the smoke-blackened jackets perfectly clean.

'Mm...!' She reached for her cup and gulped down a draught of cool milk. 'That was fantastic!'

'You'll get fat.' Sardonically Rolf eyed her slender body enveloped by the voluminous jumper. 'Tomorrow we shall have to begin living on the land, our stock of meat is almost finished.'

She was too comfortably full, too warm and cosy to pay attention to his words. Firelight was flickering against her cheeks and it was too much of an effort even to exert the small amount of pressure required to rock the chair. Once again her eyelids drooped, and when she heard music she thought she was dreaming. But then Rolf's pleasantly-timbred voice, run through with an undertone of amusement, began singing in French to the accompaniment of an ancient melodion, alerting her ears with the sound of her name.

'A la claire fontaine
M'en allant promener
J'ai trouvé l'eau si belle
Que je m'y suis baigné.
Il y a longtemps que je t'aime,
Jamais je ne t'oublierai.'

She waited until the song was finished, then lifted her lashes and saw him sitting opposite, fire flame reflecting in the depths of his eyes.

'What do the words mean?' she asked, curious but shy. 'Will you translate them?'

She suspected that he had fully intended doing so, and felt dominated when, held by his intense, fire-flecked look, he softly explained.

'*A la Claire Fontaine*—At the Clear Running Fountain—is a song that was so beloved of the earlier voyageurs it eventually came to be regarded as the French-Canadians' unofficial anthem. It tells the tale of a voyageur who stopped by a clear running fountain and finding it beautiful bathed in it. As he dried himself beneath an oak tree he heard a nightingale singing high in its branches with a heart as gay as his own was sad, for he had lost his lady love. She had asked for a bouquet of roses, which he had refused to give her, and he was regretting his refusal bitterly because he had realised that,' his voice suddenly deepened, 'he would always love her, never forget her, and he wished that the flowers that had caused his downfall could be confined to the depth of the ocean.'

Claire blushed, very conscious of an atmosphere of deep intimacy filling the shadow-shrouded room. She reacted with a flippancy deliberately contrived to combat the threat of hidden danger.

'Pigheaded stubbornness seems to be a failing of your race,' she jibed. 'The wealthy, arrogant voyageur could probably have afforded to buy armfuls of roses, yet he preferred to dig in his heels, simply to demonstrate who was master.'

'Are you drawing a parallel?' he drawled. 'Telling me that unless I accede to your wishes I'll be left bitterly regretting the loss of my love?' He stood up, casting his tall shadow over her crouching form, but when he took a step towards her she jumped to her feet and ran, overlooking in her haste the thick hooked mat that stretched the width of the floor. It tripped her like an unseen foot, sending her sprawling in a heap at the foot of the bedroom door.

Unmindful of dignity, she scrambled upright and fled into her bedroom, pressing her hands against her ears to shut out the sound of Rolf's humiliating laughter.

The sun had risen hours before she ventured out of her bedroom the next morning. She dallied deliberately, waiting until she heard him striding off towards the smithy where yesterday he had spent much of his time experimenting with an assortment of antiquated equipment, then, feeling the humiliated heat would never fade from her cheeks, she crept into the kitchen and began foraging in the dresser for flour, hoping to work off her frustration by copying Rolf's method of making sourdough.

Suddenly the chickens scratching around the door of the cottage began squawking, setting up an ear-splitting din that sent her rushing outside to find out the cause of their obvious panic. Birds were scattering in all directions when she flung open the door, all except the one Rolf was clutching by the scruff of its neck.

He grinned at the sight of her, then nodded down

at the struggling bird. 'I think I've managed to pick out the plumpest. We'll stuff it with hot stones and bury it in a pit, if it's left to cook slowly we'll have a moist, succulent bird for dinner.'

A red haze swam in front of her eyes. 'You'll do no such thing, you, you ... callous barbarian! That's Henry—put him down, and don't you dare to so much as ruffle a feather!'

His astonishment would have been comical if she had been in a mood to appreciate it. Sounding full of amused amazement, he protested, 'To survive in remote areas one must become conditioned to regarding anything that swims, flies or runs as a moving meal ticket!'

'Not the chickens,' she insisted stubbornly. 'I've christened each one of them, if I had to eat one I'd feel like a cannibal!'

To her horror her voice wobbled and tears—so huge and forceful they could not be blinked back —flooded into her eyes.

Immediately he realised that she was genuinely upset, he relented. 'Very well, gentle heart, they'll be reprieved, but only on condition that you come with me and help me trap some other kind of game.'

Very reluctantly she agreed to accompany him to the surrounding fields where, in selected spots, he laid down his snares. As they lay in waiting in the long grass with the breeze in their faces and sun beaming upon their backs, he whispered:

'If you see an animal lifting its head, freeze— that's a sure sign that our potential victim is worried.'

'The snares won't inflict pain, I hope?' she

pleaded, her eyes troubled.

Seemingly insensitive he chuckled. 'There are four tried and trusted ways of catching food and they can be summed up as: tangle, mangle, dangle and strangle. A tangle snare is a trip wire with a pit to drop the victim in; a dangle trap is one where the animal runs into it and is caught by a loop and is then either hoisted up in the air or hanged. A mangle trap drops something heavy on to its victim and strangling is, of course, carried out by hand.'

Unaware of her horrified stare, he continued keeping a sharp lookout for signs of movement, ignorant of the fact that she was classing him in her mind with Indians who were at least able to make survival their excuse for seizing anything made of flesh as potential food.

Instinctively she tensed at the sight of movement in the grass where the snares had been laid. Five little brown furry bodies with white pompom tails were bobbing their way into danger, a group that looked to her fevered imagination like a mother with a brood of playful children. Nothing on earth could have prevented her from reacting as she did. Jumping to her feet, she clapped her hands in frenzied warning and yelled:

'Go back! Oh, *please* go back...!'

'Claire, what the blazes...!' Rolf jumped to his feet and grabbed her furiously by the shoulders.

To her own surprise and his, her eyes once again flooded with tears. For a long time he stared darkly, then with a groan of remorse he pulled her into his arms and turned her bones to water with a ragged apology.

'Hell, I'm sorry—I always seem to be giving you the rough end of my tongue! Don't cry, gentle heart, please don't cry.'

He held her loosely within arms that for once did not seem demanding, but gently protective. Claire yielded to an inner force urging her to rest her head upon his accommodating chest and felt the thud of his heartbeats linking up with her own to form a throbbing duet that pounded in her ears. His hold did not tighten, it was as if, conscious of her fawn-like timidity, he was afraid that one hasty movement, one hint of hazard, would startle her out of his grasp and so, being a man of the woodland versed in the ways of nervous creatures, had decided to discard force in favour of the kind of patience and kindness that tames small creatures into taking food from an outstretched hand.

He neither spoke nor moved while she wrestled with her bewilderment, wondering why, though she had not cried since she was a child, twice in the space of an hour, she should have indulged in the weakness of tears; why his torn apology should have plucked such a response from her heartstrings and why, when all she wanted was to be rid of him, she should have been made to feel so utterly secure by the drumming of his powerful heartbeats.

'Claire...!' His voice could not have been steadier, yet it contained a nuance, a hint of barely controlled frustration that caused her to freeze. When his head lowered nearer she did not wait to give him the benefit of the doubt, but jerked out of reach and with a startled, accusing look spun on her heel and began racing, panicky as a startled rabbit, across the fields.

Half an hour later as she sat gazing out of the window of the cottage, mulling over the confusing, strangely poignant interlude, she was jerked into awareness by a query directed from the open doorway.

'Pleasant thoughts...?'

She blushed, wondering what conclusion he was drawing from her daydreaming, from her vacant smile as she sat staring into space.

He was lounging in the doorway, one shoulder supported against a jamb, his hands thrust deep into the pockets of disreputable jeans that he had rolled up to his knees, showing a length of brown calf and bare feet crossed at the ankles. She barely spared him a glance, being already too aware of his look of superb fitness, of the leashed virility contained within powerful chest and shoulders. '*There is a beast inside every man that has to be subdued, whipped and tamed,*' he had once admitted. Was the beast ready to purr, or to growl?

'I was wondering ...' he surprised her by sounding diffident if such an adjective could ever be applied to him, '... if you would care to come for a sail?'

Biting back a too eager acceptance, she murmured without turning her head, 'That would be nice. Can you spare me a few minutes to change into a more suitable outfit?'

She did not stop to analyse her emotions as eagerly she threw her dress over her head and began searching through her suitcase for slacks. 'He has a preference for bright colours,' she found herself murmuring, discarding subdued browns and creams. She pounced upon a playsuit that had been bought in a rare mood of abandon; when she had tried it on at home she had decided that the bright red shade drained her face of colour and that the skimpy shorts and halter top laid unflattering emphasis upon too-slender limbs and gently-rounded curves. But this time she had to reverse her opinion, for the bright colour looked startlingly flattering against a contrasting tan that had built up imperceptibly during days of glorious weather and the cut of the suit seemed to emphasise perfectly a perkily-rounded bottom and breasts full and firm as pomegranates straining against the confines of the brief top.

Feeling shy and not a little self-conscious, she eventually nerved herself to step outside her bedroom and walk across the kitchen towards Rolf. She steeled herself to rebuff any satirical reference to the scantiness of her outfit, but was unaccountably hurt when at first sight of her his dark eyes grew bleak and hard lines of tension formed around his mouth.

'You certainly know how best to punish a man,' he accused in the tight tone of voice he had adopted since the moment he had assumed that his shouting had frightened her. 'I think I'd rather cope with ostracism than with deliberate provocation!'

They set off in silence to climb a path leading up to cliffs ablaze with gorse and heather, picking their way carefully between fissures that looked as if they might have been formed by a giant hand directing a karate chop, splitting the cliffs from top to bottom into deep, dangerous chasms, and as carefully they negotiated the widest splits in the rock he took her hand and did not let go until they had descended the path inclining steeply towards the shore.

Pulled up on to the shingle beneath the cliffs was a small dinghy set upon a launching trolley. Rolf left her to see to the rigging, so she began beach-combing, searching deep pools for sea-urchins and starfish, pouncing upon a glint of emerald poking through the grey shingle, then feeling slightly fool-ish when all she unearthed was a green glass float from a trawl net.

'I see you still nurture childish hopes of finding pieces of eight or treasure from some old galleon,' Rolf chuckled behind her. Claire spun round, startled, and felt bound to defend herself against his mocking derision.

'It's possible—everyone knows that a ship of the Spanish Armada was shipwrecked off the Head. You wouldn't be so quick to sneer if I turned up some ducats.'

'Or even a bottle of rum from an old galleon?' he laughed aloud, looking more relaxed than he had done all day. 'The boat's ready, let's make our way across to the island.'

Before the dinghy was launched he insisted upon her donning a lifejacket, then briefly explained the working of the boat and outlined what he wanted her to do.

'Dinghies usually have a crew of two. Instead of having heavy keels to keep them upright, they have small wooden boards known as centreboards which stop the boat from being blown sideways by the wind. Once we're afloat we may have to hang right outside the boat to stop it from overturning—but don't be afraid,' he soothed, reading correctly her look of apprehension, 'I have no intention of allowing you to drown.'

The thrill of skimming the waves behind a billowing sail was completely new to her. Rolf left her no time to feel apprehensive as expertly he beat to windward, snapping out orders to shift her weight from one side of the dinghy to the other as he changed tack, steering right across the wind. Deeply absorbed, she was taken completely by surprise when the island loomed, appearing like a gigantic horse rising from the sea, with nose still submerged. Inexpert as she was, she could appreciate the superb seamanship Rolf displayed as he steered the dinghy through the small 'eye' and guided it towards the rocky shore.

'Did you enjoy your sail, *mon amie*?' His teeth flashed startling white when he grinned and held out his arms to lift her ashore.

Claire hesitated, mistrusting the air of jaunty satisfaction that seemed to have sprung from his tussle with the tides; he had challenged nature and predictably he had won. But then Rolf Ramsey always had to win.

Accepting the futility of trying to argue with the man glinting up at her, his straddled legs knee-deep in water, she lowered herself cautiously into his arms and felt an immediate shock when she was grabbed and held unnecessarily close to his bared, muscular chest.

'It would help,' he suggested, mildly amused, 'if

you could bring yourself to put your arms around my neck.'

When reluctantly she slid an arm loosely around his shoulder he punished her by pretending to let her slip. With a gasp of alarm she flung both arms tightly around his neck and hung on.

'That's much better, *chérie*,' he murmured wickedly, making no effort to move, thoroughly enjoying her embarrassment as he cradled her close with quirked lips hovering a fraction above her quivering mouth. Fear rushed back in full force, fear that her will would not be strong enough to withstand the pressure of his mouth, fear that the weakening ache stirring within her depths would spread its dangerous euphoria throughout her traitorous body.

'Claire,' he whispered, dark eyes smouldering, 'when will you admit that you were born for the sole purpose of becoming my wife?'

She snapped the fraught tension by grating, 'I doubt very much if Jonathan would agree with that theory!'

For a second she seemed in danger of being dumped into the sea. She had made him furiously angry, as she always did whenever she mentioned Jonathan's name, but he managed to swallow back an angry reply and began wading, bleak-eyed, towards the shore.

While he made fast the dinghy she ran up a path soaring the height of the cliff, then disappeared at the top into a blaze of gorse and heather. Feeling free as a bird newly released from a cage, she raced without stopping until she ran out of island, halting

at the edge of cliffs shaped like outstretched arms
flung around a small, sandy cove. Feeling like a
castaway on a deserted island, with only the sky
above and miles of empty sea at her feet, she picked
her way down to the shore, then, hot and exhausted,
stretched full length upon a comfortable bed of
sand.

An hour must have passed before she raised her
head. Amazed at the number of catnaps in which
she had seemingly begun to indulge, she struggled
upright feeling hot, sticky and completely unre-
freshed. She gazed out to sea, her attention caught
by a seal-dark head bobbing above the water, then
when an upraised arm waved she realised that it
was Rolf frolicking with obvious enjoyment. She
glared resentful envy when his voice carried clear
across the water.

'Come and join me, this is an experience that
shouldn't be missed!'

'I didn't bring a bathing suit, as you very well
know!' she snapped, brushing caked sand from
bared shoulders.

'Neither did I!' was his shocking reply. 'But you
needn't let that stop you from swimming—I promise
not to look!'

Doubtfully, she watched as he began swimming,
powerful as a seal, towards the open sea, yearning
to follow his advice yet suspicious of his motives. His
head was a mere speck upon the ocean when aggra-
vation and envy overruled her doubts and she
amazed herself by flinging off her sunsuit and running with panic-stricken haste to cover her immod-
esty in a strip of cool blue sea.

The glorious freedom of swimming in the nude was a revelation to her. Never would she have believed that a skimpy bathing suit could, by comparison, feel like constricting armour. She swam around in circles, enjoying the sensual caress of the sea rippling, massaging, cooling her body, all the time keeping a wary eye open for the sight of a seal-lithe body veering shorewards. But after a while it became easy to imagine that she was the only creature left in an isolated world. In an excess of enjoyment, she kicked out, then rolled over on to her back to float blissfully, like a figurehead relinquished by the sea, a curved statuette carved out of ivory with, streaming from a shapely head, a mass of rippling golden hair.

It was only when she felt her hair tugged that she realised she was no longer alone. Twisting his fingers among the strands, Rolf tugged so that she was submerged, then allowed her to surface, spluttering.

Liar! Cheat...!' she choked, her eyes afire with a fury her father would not have recognised. 'I ought to have guessed you had no intention of keeping your word!'

Tossing back his brown spray-splashed face, he shouted with laughter that terrified her, the confident, exultant laughter of a hunter bearing down on his prey. There was no way of escape, for to have fled naked on to the beach would only have served to inflame him more. She was treading water, glaring disgust at his duplicity, when his legs snaked around hers, tightly as the tentacles of an octopus. Wildly she threshed water, but her hair was caught in a determined hand that drew her inexorably forward until their bodies were close, intimate as a hand inside a glove.

He was holding her head above water, yet she felt the panicky sensation of drowning as a rushing sound deafened her ears and a red mist swam before her eyes while she endured caresses so tender, so sensual, it was impossible to guess where his touch ended and the sea's began.

She was afire, yet shivering, when he lifted her into his arms and carried her out of the water. She kept her eyes closed, but felt the warmth of sand against her back when he dropped to his knees and lowered her gently on to the beach. The pressure of his body, seal-smooth and supple, his urgent, desirous mouth, aroused in her a force of exquisite, almost unendurable feeling.

'Give in, *mon ange*,' he said huskily, his voice brine-hoarsened, 'lower the barriers of pride and admit, my divinely lovely virgin bride, that you are aching to be made a wife.'

He could not have known how near she came to succumbing to temptation. Only the reminder that he had resorted to marriage simply as a means of obtaining something he coveted held her on the brink of sanity. '*I always get what I want!*' he had said. But after the honeymoon, what then? Neglect, indifference, even downright resentment?

Years of strictly enforced discipline enabled her to subdue some of the fire in her veins, helped her to control the trembling of her body until she lay like a statue beneath him, cold and still as marble.

Her voice was a mere thread of sound, but run

through with such contempt that a tight band of pain formed around his mouth. 'I despise you, Rolf Ramsey, for breaking your word. Only two nights ago you promised never to force me to become your wife!'

Slowly he released her, and in that poignant moment it hardly seemed to matter that both her body and her emotions were laid bare. Eyeing her with a grimness that seemed at the same time sad, he tersely contradicted, 'I have not broken my word, and as for my promise never to force you physically to carry out the duties of a wife, I have not changed my mind—*I did not promise, however, never to try to make you change yours!*'

CHAPTER TEN

By the end of the week Margot had become a firm friend and seemed anxious to show her appreciation of Claire's regular attendance by increasing her supply of milk little by little each day.

On her way to minister to the goat, Claire rounded the corner of an outhouse, bucket in one hand, stool in the other, and stopped dead at the sight of a small brown furry bundle that was struggling ineffectually to rise to its feet and follow its mother, a Loghtan ewe, and its twin sister who were ambling slowly out of sight. She had named the twins Pete and Polly, and immediately she dropped to her knees beside the lamb she recognised that it was Pete who was in trouble. The attitude of the ewe who, seemingly deaf to her son's plaintive baas, continued ambling away, struck Claire as extremely callous.

Flushed with indignation, she consoled the lamb and supported his hindquarters to help him upright. For a moment he maintained a drunken sort of balance, then to her dismay he flopped weakly to the ground and resumed his pitiful bleating.

'Oh, Pete, what's wrong...?' Anxiously she stroked his downcast head and ran her fingers through fleece so brown and thick she was reminded of a cuddly bear cub. Frustrated by her inability to help the stricken animal, she looked around for

Rolf, then, hearing the sound of metal upon metal, she abandoned the pail and milking stool and ran towards the smithy.

She discovered him stripped to the waist bending over an anvil set into a massive tree-trunk block in the centre of the earth floor. He turned without noticing her to grasp the handle of an ancient pair of bellows placed next to the forge and as he directed a draught of air on to the white-hot fire sparks flew out and the fireglow intensified, highlighting rivulets of sweat trickling down his brown torso.

He could be the devil stoking the fires of hell! Claire thought, then immediately felt ashamed. Since the day of their outing to the island he had treated her with extreme kindness, ministering to her comfort, anticipating her every wish, being careful not to display any word, look or action that might disrupt the tenor of their precarious, newly-established truce. She glanced around, taking in the cooling tank in its rough setting of stones, at walls covered by horseshoes, tools and miscellaneous gear, at a massive nail-studded bench with tools scattered over its surface, and wondered what it was that necessitated his spending hours inside the smithy, hammering at the anvil like a man demented, returning to the cottage only when it grew too dark to work looking spent and at times even exhausted.

'Rolf...!' She found it quite easy now to address him by name.

Though she had spoken quietly his head jerked erect as if his keen ears were attuned to react immediately to the sound of her voice.

'I'm worried about Pete,' she appealed, 'I'm certain he's not well, have you time to come and look at him?'

'Pete being one of your four-footed friends, I presume?' He spared her one of the grave smiles that caused her heart to somersault. 'How many times have I warned you, Claire, that it's a mistake to make pets of farm animals? There's always a percentage of loss among young stock, to treat them like babies is to lay up for yourself unnecessary heartbreak.' Nevertheless, he abandoned the anvil and reached for a shirt hung upon a nail, slinging it scarfwise around his neck.

'Shouldn't you put it on?' she cautioned impulsively, then conscious that she had sounded full of wifely concern she rushed on, embarrassed, 'I'm sorry, I was forgetting that you almost make a virtue of self-denial.'

Rolf drew in a knife-sharp breath and for a moment seemed on the verge of verbal retaliation, but to her relief his stoked-up heat subsided. Coolly laconic, he reproved, 'you make me sound like a masochist—perhaps you have a point, because I doubt whether my worst enemy could have designed for me a situation worse than the one I've inflicted upon myself. It must be far easier for a man to become a monk in his old age.'

There was no trace of tension in his fingers as he ran them over the lamb they discovered lying on the exact spot where she had left him. Claire tried to help him to his feet, but Rolf frowned his objection.

'Leave him—I suspect his lameness may be due to bone weakness, therefore the slightest exertion could result in his breaking a limb. Even so, he must be separated from the rest of the flock and fed. He's plump enough, too plump in fact, yet I suspect he's undernourished. Do you know if his twin is in a similar condition?'

'Indeed she is not!' she replied indignantly, 'Polly is bursting with health!'

'Polly...?' he queried weakly.

'That's what I call his sister,' she replied defensively, determined to ignore his ridicule. 'And as for his mother, I can't even begin to understand her cruel indifference!'

'You might find it easier,' he was obviously striving for patience, 'if you stop crediting animals with human attributes. Animals can feel pain and discomfort, but not emotions of joy, sorrow and least of all of guilt!'

'I'm not convinced,' she flashed, stubborn chin outthrust. 'Only the animals themselves can tell us for sure, so until a method of communication has been devised I prefer to act upon my own belief.'

As she glared at him across the prostrate lamb Rolf shrugged impatiently, yet his voice sounded gentle as he reminded. 'So be it, but please bear in mind that nature has her own way of reducing the size of the animal kingdom. The weak seldom survive—the ewe knows and accepts this fact, which is why she has abandoned this little one to its fate and is concentrating all her attention upon the stronger twin.'

'You mean,' Claire gulped, grey eyes enormous, 'that Pete is going to die?'

'He very well might,' he replied, his steady eyes

daring her to become emotional, 'but if he does, it will only be after we've done everything possible to save him. Our first priority is to put him some- where warm, once that's been done we'll try to tempt him to eat. The poor mite is partially weaned, but we'll try him with a little warm, sweet milk laced with a half teaspoon of whisky.'

'Let's take him into the cottage,' she gasped, choked with pity.

He frowned. 'I'm not sure that's advisable— animals thrive best in their own environment. I was thinking more along the lines of building a small covered pen in a well-sheltered part of the farm.'

'Oh, but ...' she swallowed back fierce, argu- mentative words and decided instead to plead, 'he may need attention during the night, it would be much more convenient to have him near at hand, don't you think?'

To her relief Rolf seemed inclined to be swayed. 'All right, we'll try him inside for just one night, then if there are signs of improvement we can move him outside in the morning.'

When he lifted the lamb gently into his arms she ran on ahead to feed peat on to the fire and by the time he entered the cottage she was kneeling on an outspread blanket waiting to cosset the ailing lamb. Anxiously she waited, soothing the lamb by stroking his coat and whispering soft words of com- fort while Rolf prepared a stimulant of whisky, sugar and diluted milk, then poured it warm into a teacup. By this time the lamb had ceased baaing and was curled, a shivering crescent of misery, with eyes closed and one hoof tucked in a beguiling pose beneath its vulnerable chin.

Claire would have been loath to disturb him, but predictably Rolf seemed to suffer no such qualms. Kneeling on the right side of Pete, he spanned the lamb's nose with a finger and thumb, placed a finger in his mouth, then tilted the cup so that the doctored milk began trickling slowly down his throat. The lamb began to cough, discharging most of the medicine which ran in a milky stream out of the side of his mouth.

'We'll try feeding with a teaspoon,' Rolf decided. 'Fetch one from the dresser, will you?'

But this method was equally unsuccessful. The lamb appeared to be too weak even to swallow.

'Let me try!' Claire pushed him aside, dipped a finger into the milk and transferred it to Pete's mouth. For a second there was no response, but just as she was about to give up she felt the beginnings of a tentative suck. With a cry of delight she again dipped her finger into the milk and this time was rewarded by a weak but definite suck. 'It's working!' she cried, turning shining eyes upon Rolf. 'Does that mean he's going to get better?'

He seemed undecided how to reply and to her ears sounded over-cautious when he hedged, 'To keep up that sort of feeding would take up twenty-four hours of each day and even if you should do so there is no guarantee that he'll recover, though I'm certain you're determined to tire yourself out in the attempt. Try to be sensible, Claire, let me experiment with the orthodox method before you commit yourself to unnecessary effort.'

'No!' her voice rang true as steel. 'Your way upsets him, and anyway I don't think the effort *is* unnecessary—look how strongly he's sucking! I'm convinced that by this time tomorrow we'll see a noticeable improvement—and if nursing can help we *certainly* will!'

It was a slow and arduous task that she had set herself. After an hour her back began to ache as she maintained her crouched position over the lamb and the finger she was using as a dipper began to feel numb. Nevertheless, without thought for her own discomfort she continued feeding, determined not to become disheartened even though the level of milk in the cup showed little evidence of sinking.

Rolf hovered in the background but made no attempt to interfere, seemingly sensitive to her desire to cope alone, to prove herself capable of carrying out to its conclusion the job she had undertaken. 'It's not simply a case of wanting to prove myself right,' she assured herself as solemn-faced she bent over her patient, 'but it would be nice to be able to convince Rolf that I'm not as useless as he must imagine me to be. Everyone has some special talent—my sourdough is unexceptional; more often than not I burn the meat, and I'm so clumsy with the cooking pots that he's practically taken over the whole of the cooking himself, but I'm convinced that I can make Pete well again, and if I manage it there'll be the extra bonus of having earned a little of his respect'. Yet it went without saying that her care of the lamb would have been no less tender, no less conscientious even without an extra incentive.

When Rolf lit the lamp she looked up, bemused, her cheeks fire-flushed, finding it incredible that so many hours should have passed unnoticed when each second had marked only the weak beating of Pete's heart and the almost imperceptible panting of his breath.

Rolf's shadow loomed. 'Leave him now.' He bent to help her to her feet. 'He needs sleep—the greatest healer of all.'

Accepting the truth of his argument, Claire obeyed without question and was glad of his help to stand erect and stretch her aching limbs. He was still lightly supporting her when she looked up into his eyes and smiled.

'*Dooiney Mooar.*' Lapsing without thought into her native tongue, she managed, quite unintentionally, to disconcert him. He looked dazzled, unable to tear his eyes away from rose-flushed cheeks, eyes grey and glowing as mist wreathing dawning sunrise, and a mouth, soft, tremulous, uncertain, directing for the very first time a smile especially for his benefit. A muscle leapt to life in his jaw; his voice, though mild, sounded leashed when steadily he tilted:

'Are you swearing at me?'

Her involuntary gurgle of laughter did not disturb the lamb but had a peculiar effect upon Rolf, who could not have been more transfixed if the legendary 'lil folk' themselves—local fairies dressed in green and red who danced in the valleys and glens and swam in the waterfalls—had trooped into the cottage. They too, it was said, could wither with a glance anyone who displeased them but, conversely, those upon whom they smiled became their slaves for life.

Unaware that the impact of her smile had set his senses reeling, she explained a trifle shyly, '*Dooiney Mooar* is Manx for "big man". The words sprang to mind when I saw your shadow looming upon the wall,' she faltered lamely.

With a lightness of touch that betrayed his anxiety that the newly-spun thread of intimacy should not be broken, Rolf guided her towards the table and encouraged cautiously, 'There must be many gaps in my knowledge of the island and its people, gaps that you seem more than qualified to fill. The loghtan sheep, for instance, can you tell me anything about the breed?'

The faint implication that whatever she could remember might help to influence Pete's recovery was enough to set her mind searching. She washed her hands, then sat down, brow wrinkled, and waited until he had dished out their meal.

'All I know is that the loghtan is an ancient breed that has dwindled over the years and now exists only in very small numbers in the island. They are noted for their extreme agility and also, of course, for the distinctive warm brown colour of their fleece which has been compared with the colour of unbleached bitter almonds and Spanish snuff. Loghtan is a Manx word derived from *lugh* (mouse) and *dhoan* (brown) and is generally used to describe anything that's tawny brown. Even historians are undecided about the origins and history of the breed, which is supposed to be very similar to sheep native to Iceland, the Faroes, the Shetlands and the

Outer Hebrides. Some reckon they might have been brought to the island by Vikings as early as the ninth century and others argue that they may be descended from the flocks of the native Celts. So now you can understand our determination not to allow the breed to die out.'

A shadow darkened Rolf's face as he slewed a look towards the sleeping lamb. 'So that's the explanation,' he expelled a slow breath. 'I should have guessed!'

'Guessed what?' Her voice sharpened. 'Pete's ailment, d'you mean? Do you think you know what's wrong with him?'

'You've given me a clue,' he admitted, causing her heart to sink as she read an emotion akin to pity in his expression. 'He shows all the symptoms of rickets, a disease caused through feeding off land that has a deficiency of particular elements necessary to produce a perfect offspring. Food grown on light, moor tillage land dressed with lime is said to aggravate the condition—that, together with constant in-and-in breeding.'

'Rickets?' her brow knitted. 'Isn't that something babies used to get?'

'And still do, among the poorer classes of society,' he reminded her grimly. 'It's still prevalent among the children of tribal Indians.'

'But it can be cured, surely?' she insisted eagerly.

'Provided there are no complications, I believe the disease can be halted by giving the patient a sufficiency of fat—cream, oil, anything of that nature will do—by complete rest and strangely enough by providing plenty of light, either sunshine or artificial. Fresh air is also advisable, but as I'm suspicious of the lamb's dry cough he'd better remain indoors for tonight at least.'

Once the dinner dishes had been washed and tidied away they settled down to keep vigil over the lamb that Claire knelt to comfort each time its small pot-belly heaved when he coughed. Rolf tried insisting, pleading, then finally bullying in an effort to get her to go to bed.

'Even if you lie down fully dressed you'll feel the benefit,' he coaxed. 'I promise to waken you the moment I see the slightest change in his condition.'

'Pete is my patient,' she insisted adamantly, 'and I will nurse him through the night.'

Exasperated by her stubbornness, Rolf finally gave in. From the depths of the dresser he unearthed a bottle of cod liver oil and managed to coax a couple of spoonfuls down Pete's reluctant throat. Then he positioned the oil lamp so that its beam created a halo of light around the lamb's head before carefully banking up the fire to ensure regular heat throughout the night.

Eyeing Claire sitting tensely upright with her eyes fastened upon the sleeping lamb, he held out his hand with the carefully casual suggestion, 'Come and sit with me on the settle. If we're to remain in here all night we might as well make ourselves as comfortable as possible.'

To his surprise, she did not hesitate, but crossed, heavy-eyed, to sit beside him on the hard, cushionless settle and did not attempt to fight off the arm he placed around her shoulders or the hand that drew her head down until it was resting in the hollow of his shoulder. All day the weather had been threatening to break, and as the first drops of rain splattered against the windowpanes she snuggled closer with a sigh of contentment, feeling the room, its quietness complete except for the constant heavy ticking of the ancient clock, to be full of ghosts—happy, benevolent ghosts.

'Tell me about the people who used to live here,' she murmured, 'were they happy, do you suppose?'

'What is happiness?' The thought crossed her mind that Rolf sounded far less relaxed than she felt. 'What is regarded as good fortune by one can be considered a disaster by another. According to his descendants, who I must admit could have been biased, Angus Ramsey, who inherited this croft from his father, was something of a scribe and was far more interested in making small wood carvings such as you see around you in the cottage and in fashioning hats and creels out of straw rope than he was in farming. He bequeathed to his family many small diaries inside which he had written that his mother worked hard in the home as well as doing a stint in the fields, and that their neighbours were kind, thoughtful folk who all helped one another to sow the crops and to harvest and stack the corn. They gathered around their firesides in winter to gossip and to retell ancient tales such as the one about the *buggane* that haunted the caves at the Black Head, or of the old *karrans*, powerful giants who were said to be descended from the Armada Spaniards who were supposedly wrecked upon Spanish Head. The youngsters gathered separately in another house to sing and dance and no doubt to pair up and do their courting. So you see, it's hard to judge in which circumstances happiness may be found, for although Angus Ramsey became a wealthy man, nostalgia for the old days is evident in every page of his diaries.'

'We're slow to recognise happiness until it's lost,' Claire proffered dreamily, appreciative of the harmony that had taken the place of discord.

'A lot depends upon ourselves,' he cautioned, handling the subject as if it were fine crystal liable to shatter into a thousand sharp splinters under undue pressure. 'Obviously you possess a depth of maternal feeling that will remain a barrier to your happiness until you find some object upon which it can be lavished. You need a child, Claire,' he finally dared to challenge, keeping his eyes fastened upon a space above her head.

He braced for the inevitable spate of scorn, but glanced down hopefully when she remained silently content within the circle of his arm. Gold-dusted lashes were fanning her cheeks, her breast was rising and falling in time with her even breathing, and her mouth was curved upwards, smiling as if pleasant dreams were invading her deep exhausted sleep ...

CHAPTER ELEVEN

THE first thing Claire saw when she awoke was the blue elk medallion a mere inch from her cheek that was burrowed, hotly flushed, against the rock-hard surface of Rolf's chest. For a second her mind remained fuddled, unable to offer an explanation as to why she should be lying in his arms inside a kitchen shrouded in nocturnal shadows. Then a sound impinged upon her conscience, a weak paroxysm of coughing followed by the pitiful, panting gasps of a lamb fighting for breath.

She jerked erect to glare accusingly into Rolf's sombre face. 'Why didn't you waken me!'

'There was no point.' He sounded strained, extremely uptight, which caused her to wonder if he were not as insensitive as he had implied to the appeal of delicate creatures. Unaccountably, she felt deprived when he removed his arm from around her shoulders and stood upright. As she sensed his mood of savage impatience, her indignation was replaced by concern.

'I'm sorry for being so selfish,' she faltered.

'In what way were you selfish?' he questioned tightly, stepping up to the fireplace to hook the kettle on to the *slouree* without even glancing her way.

'By falling asleep and neglecting my patient,' she spelled out quietly, 'by pandering to my own needs at the expense of your own.'

His head lifted sharply to direct a dark-eyed, penetrating stare. 'I'd begun to think you haven't the least inkling of a man's needs, that you imagined me to be some kind of automaton, designed to be made use of during the day, then stacked away in some convenient corner at night.'

Bewildered by his sudden change of attitude and unnerved by the restless manner in which he had begun to prowl the room, she queried, heart in mouth, 'Aren't men's needs basically the same as women's? Each of us needs sleep, and warmth, and comfort.' Feeling an urge to be kind, she suggested impulsively, 'Why not make use of my bed while I stay on watch, you can't possibly have felt relaxed during the nights you've spent lying with nothing but a sleeping bag between you and bare boards. Don't try to deny that I'm right!' she continued swiftly, almost gaily, when he seemed prepared to argue. 'I've heard you prowling restlessly at night and letting yourself out of the cottage at daybreak to go down to the beach for an early swim.'

When he loomed out of the shadows to stand glowering down at her she gasped, feeling her breath severed as if by the flick of a hunting knife.

'Mon dieu!' he blistered, 'what narrow depths of understanding you possess! In exchange for being used as a flaccid, accommodating pillow I'm to be allowed the privilege of occupying your bed—*alone* —while you remain in here lavishing affection upon an animal that can neither understand nor appreciate its good fortune. You work tirelessly in an effort to ease its misery, yet can conveniently

overlook mine! I suspect you're drawn towards animals because they make no demands—are you so incapable of deep emotion, Claire, that you shy away when you recognise it in others?' Without seeming to move he plucked her from the spot where she stood rooted, enclosing her within arms that hugged tightly as a bear. 'Let's find out, shall we?' he challenged thickly. 'To hell with being a gentleman, I much prefer to be the father of your son!'

His lips crushed down upon hers, injecting lusty desire into every vein, catching her so unawares she was given no time to erect a dam against the racing, roaring, boiling flood of passion that snatched her into its rapids and tossed and buffeted her until she was gasping for breath, clinging to him as desperately as the shipwrecked cling to any available spar.

Claire was ashamed of the terrible fascination he aroused whenever he lost control, of the urge she felt to discover what lay beyond the tantalising stage their relationship had reached. As his kisses drowned her in waves of sweet confusion she experienced at one moment the reckless bravery of a swimmer determined to conquer unknown seas and in the next the cowardice of a nervous beginner teetering on the edge of a diving board wondering if she were competent enough, if she would be hurt, if the dive might even prove to be fatal.

'Clear Running Water...!' A delicious thrill trembled through her body when he gently nibbled her ear. 'Pure as melted snow, cool as a mountain stream, fascinating as a waterfall plunging into mysterious, unplumbed depths! Stop this torment, Claire,' he groaned, tracing with his lips the soft,

pulsating curve of her neck. 'These past hours have
been agony, holding you close yet knowing you
were distant; being clawed by an inner war, a battle
between a mad urge to possess and a conscience that
insisted upon holding me to my promise.' His low,
shaken voice became suddenly insistent. 'Be kind
to me, Claire, as kind as you would be to any animal
in torment—put me out of my misery!'

His lips found hers, drowning the sob of in-
decision lodged like an arrow in her throat. The
emotions she had shared with Jonathan had been
nothing like this, his kisses had been chaste, making her feel adored as a remote princess set upon a
pedestal. But with Rolf she felt wanton, a sister
to the young Manx maidens who, when tossed across
the shoulders of lusty Viking raiders, had submitted
to capture with hardly a murmur.

Weakened by his forceful persuasion, she melted
against him and mercilessly he exploited her weakness by pushing away her blouse from her shoulders
and seeking every vulnerable nerve with a touch
that unearthed deeply-hidden ecstasy, and with lips
that branded his mark of possession upon every
tender hollow and curve.

'Rolf!' she gasped, attempting to plead for
mercy against such exquisite punishment. But a
madness had entered his blood, an insanity that
would be assuaged only when passion had fused
both their bodies into one.

She had just discovered the terrifying rapture of
his leaping reaction to her first shy but positive
response, when above the clamour of pounding
heartbeats she heard the plaintive cry of an animal

in distress. He must have heard it too, yet when she tried to pull away he jerked her back into his arms with the hoarse imprecation:

'*Mère de dieu*, you can't be prepared to leave me now!'

But when the cry came again, a pathetic bleat followed by a paroxysm of coughing, remorse combined with panic to give her the necessary strength to push her way out of his arms.

Trembling, dishevelled, with a cloud of golden hair falling down past one bare shoulder, she knelt to soothe and stroke the lamb. 'I'm certain he's worse,' she jerked, sounding thrashed with emotion.

But her remark was lost, drowned by the sound of a slamming door and by footsteps striding out angrily into the darkness.

Shaking with reaction, she ministered to the lamb, that small part of her mind still capable of reasoning blessing Rolf's foresight in positioning the singing kettle so that steam from its spout was feeding moisture into the air, enabling the lamb to breathe a little easier. For what seemed hours she remained crouched on her knees trying to coax Pete into accepting drops of oil or warm milk, but to no avail. His spasms of coughing grew more frequent until eventually her dismayed eyes caught sight of some substance dribbling from the side of his mouth that had no connection with any of the medicine he had been given. When finally he lapsed into exhausted sleep she sat hugging her own deprived body and took time to formulate her thoughts, to dissect with all the honesty of which she was capable, rampant emotions, now subdued to a steady pulsating throb, that needed only the sound of Rolf's voice, the crunch of his approaching footsteps, as a signal to start once more the battle to tear her apart.

'Is this love?' she murmured, feeling physically and emotionally battered. 'Can this be the emotion lovers rave about and poets find so inspiring? Surely love should be a joy, not a penance, should unite instead of tearing asunder.' Yet even in the midst of confusion she knew that she had been allowed a glimpse of paradise that fabled place wherein everything was beautiful and joyful, and where pain and suffering were unknown.

Suppressing an urge to weep, she rose to her feet, carefully banked up the fire, then after drawing the rocking chair as close as possible to the sleeping lamb, collapsed on to its hard, comfortless seat. Determined that her heavy lids should not be allowed to droop, she sat stiffly erect, levering one foot against the floor to keep the chair in constant motion. But gradually her head sank sideways, the rocker became motionless, and once again she was overwhelmed by sleep of such depth she was rendered oblivious to fingers of early morning light groping into the dark corners of the kitchen, and to the squeak of hinges on a cautiously-opened door.

She awoke with a start to the sound of bacon sizzling in a pan and to the rattle of crockery as Rolf set out breakfast dishes on the table. Sun beamed through the window, playing upon willow-patterned plates and a matching jug filled to the brim with rich, creamy milk, upon spoons hollowed out of horn and upon a vase of wild flowers, foxgloves, pennywort, and the colourful thrift that flourished in every nook and cranny of rocks towering high above the sea. Were they a peace-offering? Claire wondered, still half asleep. A wordless apology for Rolf's uncharacteristic burst of ill-temper? Perhaps he had taken to heart the moral contained in the song he was so fond of singing about the voyageur who had bitterly regretted the rift between himself and his loved one.

'If you hurry you'll have time for a shower before breakfast.' The curtness of Rolf's tone gave lie to her theory that he was in a mood of repentance. She gasped, made breathless by his cold splash of words, then jerked erect when she remembered Pete. Her eyes swivelled towards the spot where she had left him and remained staring hard at the empty space that had once held a blanket topped by the lamb's plump, brown-fleeced body.

'Where's Pete?' she gasped, rounding upon Rolf.

'I've put him outside,' he clipped, his expression unfathomable.

Not even the fact that he was still annoyed with her could repress the surge of thankfulness she felt at his words. Her grey eyes, tender as sea-mist, reflected the happiness of her serenely beautiful smile. 'He's cured!' She breathed a heartfelt sigh. 'Somehow I knew he would be, he's far too lovable to die. Where is he?' she continued eagerly. 'I'll just take a peep at him before breakfast.'

Uplifted by her sense of triumph, she could not understand why his mouth remained tense, his eyes darkly brooding.

'He's at peace, so let's leave him that way.' As if

guessing her intention to argue, he turned his attention upon the contents of the pan. 'Five more minutes and this will be ready—ample time for you to shower and dress, if you hurry!'

His attitude of urgency lent wings to her feet. Without further encouragement she sped into her bedroom, grabbed a towel and a change of clothing, then with steps as light as her spirits almost danced her way outside towards the makeshift shower.

The water inside the improvised tank had been drawn from a deep, cool well, yet as icy needles jabbed against her warm skin she spared not so much as a thought for the luxurious bathroom she had left behind—the butter-coloured tiles chosen especially to match the deep bath with twin, dolphin-shaped taps that gushed forth an endless supply of steaming water; shelves crammed with talcum and body lotions; carpet thick and green as summer grass that had enveloped her feet up to the ankles, and the piles of warm, fluffy towels. All of these she had taken for granted, yet as she fumbled for the tees with which to plug up the holes in the plastic container she felt blissfully refreshed, tingling from head to toe with health and happiness.

After gently patting her skin dry with a coarse towel, she slipped into clean underwear, pulled on a pair of curve-hugging denims and a blue cotton top, then swathed the towel turban-wise around her damp hair, intending after breakfast to sit outside in the sunshine and comb it dry.

Rolf began dishing out the meal immediately she stepped inside the kitchen. 'In that outfit, you ought to look like an urchin,' he told her dryly, 'yet in some inexplicable way you manage to retain your air of dignity. It's been said that we bring nothing into this world and take nothing out, yet I feel certain, *ma chérie*,' he spared her a sudden, brief smile, 'that when you made your entry into this world it became immediately obvious that the child being delivered was a descendant of a very proud and gifted family.'

'But has it not also been said,' she teased, eyeing her plate with healthy relish, 'that a man who prides himself on his ancestry is like a potato plant, the best part of which is underground? That would seem to indicate either that I'm half dead—or only half alive. Which is it, do you suppose?'

That she was able to tease him so easily was a measure of the progress that had been made in their relationship, yet instead of the response she expected—the appreciative glint, the crooked half-smile, the tilt of a strongly-marked eyebrow—her words provoked a puzzling wince.

Seeming forced into making a decision, Rolf pushed aside his untouched breakfast and leant across the table, fixing her with a steady eye as obliquely he intoned, 'Once, during my stint as a forest ranger, I came across a beaver pond. I moved towards it, soundless as an Indian, I thought, but I must actually have made as much noise as a bear lusting after its mate, because suddenly I heard the beaver's danger signal—a sound like the crack of a rifle shot, made by the slap of a broad, heavy tail against water. This was followed by a splash as the alarmed beavers dived to safety.'

Claire laid down her knife and fork to give him

her complete attention. Instinct told her that he was not merely making pleasant breakfast conversation, but that he had a message to impart and also that her understanding of the message was important to him.

He continued quietly, sounding as if his mind were far away, yet from the look in his eyes she guessed that he was reliving some nightmare. 'I moved out of the woodland into a clearing and saw the pond lying clear and limpid, a silver mirror with a reflection on its surface of tall spruces and in its depths the distinct outline of every submerged pebble. It was so peaceful, not so much as a breeze rustling through the trees, no lap of water, even the birds were silent. Then I spotted movement among the branches of felled trees fringing the pond and as I approached I saw a young beaver had obviously been attacked by an otter, bloody, bowed, and obviously in the last throes of death.' He hesitated, seeming to find difficulty in finding the words to go on then, sounding almost pleading, he continued, 'Instant death is merciful compared with hours of torment, Claire. In the animal world the struggle for survival is fierce, each species, however fleet of foot, however cunning, however strong, lives in fear of some predator, even the insect larva that thrives in ponds supplies the frog with food, and the frog in turn makes a meal for the snake.'

'But what about the beaver?' she urged, impatient of what seemed to be digression. 'You managed to save it, I hope?'

'If it had been possible I would have done so,'

he grated harshly, 'but as it was I had no option but to put it out of its misery as quickly and efficiently as was possible with the means available.'

'Which was...?' she questioned, feeling suddenly queasy.

'A length of twine carried for use as a snare—but only if survival should warrant it,' he stressed quickly. 'Rangers are dedicated to the saving of animal life, they will not kill unless their own lives depend upon it.'

'So you strangled the beaver,' she concluded sadly.

'Cured him,' he corrected quietly. 'Death is the cure of all pain and diseases.'

The word acted like a signal to her brain. *Cured!* He had implied that *Pete* had been cured!

Wide-eyed with horror, she jumped to her feet. 'Where's Pete?' she choked through a throat so tight she felt strangled. 'I want to see him now, *this minute!*'

'Claire...!' His look of appeal was confirmation enough. With a cry of revulsion she backed away from his outstretched hand and ran wildly out of the cottage. There were very few places where a lamb could be hidden, so desperately she ransacked with her eyes the empty outhouses, the smithy, then finally ran towards what once had been a weaver's shed that housed a loom that had sometimes been worked by candlelight, weaving flannel for seamen, petticoats for their wives, plaid bedcovers and sheets of fine Manx linen.

'Claire, don't go in there!'

Ignoring his shout, she stumbled inside and

hesitated, blinking rapidly. In the few seconds it took for her eyes to adjust to the darkened interior Rolf reached her side. Grabbing her by the shoulder, he pulled her roughly outside, but not before she had had time to notice the still form wrapped in a blanket lying in the far corner of the shed.

'*Murderer!*' she screamed, wrenching out of his arms to stumble round the corner of the shed where she was violently sick.

He was considerate enough to leave her alone until she was partially composed, yet when she finally swung her trembling body erect she was blind to the taut whiteness of his face, uncaring of the agony in his eyes. 'Please, *chérie*, try to understand why I had to do it—he had developed pneumonia and hadn't the slightest chance of making a recovery, which is why I had no alternative but to put him out of his misery.'

'You *murdered* him,' she croaked, 'simply to assuage the bloodlust of savages that runs in your veins! You killed him, like the wolf you are, viciously, coldbloodedly, because last night he dared to get in your way. Yet at the same time you've brought me alive—alive with a hatred I never dreamt myself capable of feeling for another living soul. Thank you,' she hated him with livid, tortured eyes, 'for completing my education. Before I met you I was ignorant of humiliation, degradation, and self-loathing, but with you as my teacher I've become expert at exploring the depths of shame!'

CHAPTER TWELVE

ROLF had become careless. On her way back from a long, exhausting walk Claire rounded the corner of an outhouse and saw that the car in which they had driven to the cottage had been left parked with the key still in the ignition. Dully she eyed it, insensible at first to its implications, then like a key unlocking the gates of a prison cell her mind clicked and she stared transfixed at the sleek, powerful car that suddenly represented escape into freedom, release from the nightmare situation that had erupted yesterday morning and had grown more unbearably fraught with every passing hour.

Was it really only twenty-four hours since she had discovered Pete's limp little body? she wondered, pressing shaking hands against eyes that felt sunk into her head, left dry and aching after a deluge of bewildered tears. Was it only twenty-four hours since she had discovered that the man she had married, the man whose persuasive charm had undermined her defences to such an extent she had begun to welcome his intimate caresses and savagely demanding kisses, was a monster, a wolf in sheep's clothing, so lacking in conscience and sensitivity he had not hesitated to savage the defenceless creature that had unwittingly stumbled in his path?

She hiccoughed a sob, but had no tears left to

shed; they had all been spilt yesterday, along the cliff path as she had run to put as much distance as possible between herself and Pete's slayer; on the shore where she had sat huddled for many shocked hours, impervious to chill, uncaring of the incoming tide.

The sea had been almost lapping her feet when Rolf had found her, a numbed statue of misery, on the sickle of sand that was all that was left of the bay that became submerged by each high tide. He had spared no time on words but with his face grimly set had plucked her from the sand and carried her, a struggling, screaming virago, up the treacherous cliff path. One false step would have sent them both plunging to the shore, but the touch of his hands had resurrected her into livid, hate-filled life, rendering her beyond caring.

'Don't touch me!' she had screamed in a voice so harsh and croaked it was indistinguishable from the cry of the gulls wheeling overhead. 'I can't bear your loathsome, bloodied hands!'

Impassive as an Indian chief conditioned to enduring torture without betraying pain, he had ignored her shrinking revulsion and had even mustered sufficient control to set her gently upon her feet when they were a safe distance from the jagged cliff edge.

'You're far too shocked and hungry to know what you're saying,' he had dared to pity, 'you haven't eaten a bite all day. Come along, supper's ready and waiting to be served.'

Through a red haze of anger she heard her own, wildly hysterical reply. 'And I suppose Pete is on the menu! Will you be serving him stewed, roasted or grilled?'

Then, nauseated by her own sick humour, she had clasped her hand across her mouth, stomach heaving, and aimed a last arrow of loathing before speeding off towards the cottage where she had spent the rest of the tormented night shivering in her bed.

A movement in the doorway of the cottage alerted her to the danger of allowing him to suspect her interest in the car. She dodged out of sight and re-appeared a few moments later strolling from a different direction.

'Did you enjoy your walk?' He sounded pleasantly disposed, but when she grew near she saw that his eyes held the bleakness of a man who had almost given up hope.

'Enjoy . . .?' Her voice rang hollow. 'I've forgotten the meaning of the word.'

He was blocking the doorway, so she had no choice but to wait until he decided to allow her to pass. 'I heard you go out at daybreak,' he continued, determined not to be riled 'seemingly without bothering about food. You must try to eat, Claire, otherwise you will make yourself ill.'

'Then what will you do,' she tilted hardly, 'cure by the garrotte?' She sliced a suggestive finger across her throat.

Before her hand could be lowered it was clamped within a steel-fingered vice. 'Don't try me too hard, Claire,' he warned, thin-lipped. 'You seem determined to make me lose my temper, but I'm equally determined that you will not. You've been badly shocked, naïve, cosseted child that you are, by one of the crueller facts of life, which is why I've tolerated your wild, unjust accusation, but the novelty of coping with the tantrums of a child bride is growing wearisome,' his soft, threatening tone filled her with terror, 'so I'm giving you one last chance to grow up voluntarily, the easy way. I'm going fishing,' he clamped, dropping her hand as if he felt it red hot, 'for the rest of today I shall be out in the dinghy, leaving you time to come to your senses. Make good use of your solitude, for if I return at nightfall to a sulky, sullen child you will leave me no choice but to force you into painful maturity!'

Long after he had gone Claire remained staring at the red weal curled around her wrist, a slave band impressed upon her flesh by hard possessive fingers. Tonight, with or without her consent, he intended to claim his rights, to force her into the role of a dutiful, spiritless wife. *Thank God he had forgotten about the car!*

Without waiting to pack her things, without bothering even to pin up her hair that yesterday had dried into a swirling golden cloud around her shoulders, she raced towards the car and in an ague of trembling turned the key in the ignition. Softly the engine growled into life, reminding her of the other forest predator from whom she was fleeing. Half expecting to see him loping in pursuit, she cast a nervous glance across her shoulder, then, assured that the coast was clear, she pressed down upon the clutch, engaged gear, and nervously accelerated.

She had only a vague notion of the direction in

which she should head, but as there was only a narrow lane running past the cottage she opted for returning in the direction from which they had come, knowing that beyond the stretch of moorland she would eventually come to a minor road. Although, even if Rolf should have changed his mind and returned to the cottage there was no way he could catch up with her, her heart was thumping and her palms sticky with sweat by the time she reached the road and then inevitably a signpost. The white arm pointing her way home acted like a spur, urging her to take more and more risks as she sped along deserted roads until the countryside became blessedly familiar. Hours seemed to have passed by the time she turned into a gravelled drive and drew the car to a halt before the entrance to her home. Feeling she had driven in a marathon, she forced buckling knees to support her up a flight of steps, fumbled open the door, then stumbled over the threshold.

'Good morning, *mademoiselle*, can I be of any help?' The faintly accented voice, the uplifted, finely-defined eyebrows, seemed vaguely familiar to Claire as she stared at the woman who had stepped into the hall and was looking askance, regarding her as one might a disreputable intruder.

'Who are you?' she croaked, wondering how the slim, beautifully-matured woman of fashion had come to take up residence in her father's house.

'It is I who should be asking that question, *n'est-ce pas?*' Her tinkling laughter sounded strangely out of place in surroundings which over the years had known only quiet, respectful silence.

'I belong here,' Claire replied, feeling immediately convinced that she did not.

'I don't understand,' the stranger frowned as she stepped forward. 'So far as I am aware, Monsieur Foxdale has but one daughter who, just a few days ago, was married to my son.'

'To your ... *son!*' Stupidly Claire stared at Rolf's mother, wondering how she could have overlooked their many likenesses, the twinkling eyes, the curled-up mouth, the dark hair and eyes, the very determined chin.

Unwilling comprehension had already begun to dawn in his mother's eyes when Claire stumbled forward, on the verge of collapse, and sobbed, 'I'm Claire...'

The following half hour passed as if in a dream. Afterwards she could barely recall being half carried, half pushed, towards a couch in an adjacent room, being stretched out flat with pillows tucked beneath her head, being fussed over with a concern that flooded her unhappy eyes with tears of gratitude.

'How long is it since you have eaten, *chérie?*' The question was kindly put yet demanded a truthful answer.

'Hours ... days ... oh, I'm not sure!'

'I thought as much! Stay where you are, don't dare to move,' Madame Ramsey ordered with an authority that reminded Claire of her son, 'I'll be back in a matter of minutes.'

As good as her word, she returned carrying a tray laden with a bowl of soup, a glass of milk, and a plateful of thinly sliced bread and butter.

'I do hope your father's housekeeper won't mind my taking liberties in her kitchen,' she smiled, urging Claire into a sitting position. 'She has been given the day off to attend the Tynwald Ceremony and your father is also there, so the house is empty except for myself. Fortunately, providence decreed that I should delay leaving for the ceremony until after I'd received an expected telephone call, otherwise we might have returned to find an insensible girl on the doorstep. Explanations can wait,' she scolded when Claire tried to interrupt, 'I don't want to hear a word until you've finished this soup.'

Obediently as a child Claire submitted to being spoonfed with soup and coaxed into eating bread and butter until the bowl was empty and only crumbs remained upon the plate. Feeling infinitely stronger, she settled back against the arm of the couch to sip milk that seemed bland and tasteless compared with Margot's rich, creamy offering.

Shyly she smiled at Rolf's mother, very conscious of her puzzled stare.

'Forgive me, *chérie*, but you are so totally unlike the description I have been given of my new daughter-in-law. Invariably, and with monotonous regularity, the adjectives used were: elegant, dignified, aloof, calm and, of course, very beautiful— which is the only one with which I find myself able to agree. The impression I had formed caused me to dread our first meeting because I felt sure that I would fall short of your high standards, so I can't tell you what a relief it was when a very *human* girl fell into my arms, dishevelled, wild-eyed, torn ragged with emotion. And now, *mon enfant*,' she cocked her head to one side, 'are you feeling strong enough to tell me what my clumsy, impatient son has done to bring such a look of sadness to your eyes?'

Claire found it amazingly easy to pour out her heart to the kind woman who was so sure of her place in her son's affections she was generously willing to share him. She missed out nothing, beginning with his ruthless exploitation of Jonathan's lapse; the way he had forced her into marriage against her will; the deprivation she had been made to endure in the primitive cottage and ending finally, with many gulps and sobs, by outlining the episode that had culminated in the lamb's death. Her grey eyes looked tortured as she faltered out the last pain-racked words, her eyes blurred with the dregs of tears that had been so copiously shed she felt certain she would never be capable of weeping again.

For a long time there was silence as Madame Ramsey fought unsuccessfully to control expressions of surprise, dismay, and even horror. Though her maternal pride had been shaken, her voice rang with utter disbelief when at last she managed a reply.

'I find it impossible to believe such accusations are being levelled against my son. No, no, *chérie!*' she waved a dissenting hand when Claire tried to protest. 'I do not try to suggest that you lie, merely that you must in some way have been misled, have misconstrued Rolf's motives. What have you done to each other, you two,' she threw up her hands with true Gallic excitability, 'how have you managed such a reversal of nature, turning a dignified young

woman into an hysterical wreck and a man re-
nowned for his compassion towards animals into a
slaughtering monster? Such a phenomenon is too
incredible to be believed. When Rolf telephoned
the news that he was about to be married I formed
the impression that he was very much in love with
his "princess" as he called you, and that you were
in love with him. Somewhere along the line something has gone very, very wrong.'

'Your son was never in love with me,' Claire disputed bitterly. 'He found me physically attractive,
he wanted me, and, as you are no doubt aware, he
always gets what he wants.'

'And usually deserves what he gets,' his mother
assured her quietly, 'because once he has decided
that something is worth fighting for he dedicates
heart and mind to his cause. Both animals and
humans have benefited from his dogged determination to right any wrong, he fought a hard battle
with the authorities until conservation laws were introduced and some species of animals threatened
by extinction were declared protected. The in-
justices suffered by the Indians were always to him
a festering sore and they, too, have cause to feel
grateful for the single-minded manner in which
he fought for rights which otherwise they might
never have achieved. Even as a boy,' her eyes became misty, 'he was passionately dedicated to easing
the suffering of injured animals, our home became
a hospital for the halt, lame and blind, a place of
healing from which the timid gained strength and
where the wild invariably became tame. Yet there
was a time, *ma chérie*, when for his own sake I

thought seriously of forbidding further activity because even though he achieved such a high rate of success I many times discovered him in bed sobbing over the loss of an animal that had been too far gone to benefit from his care. So you see, knowing my son as I do, I cannot accept that he would do deliberate harm to any living creature.'

'I've seen him myself,' Claire insisted shakily, strangely eager to be convinced, 'setting snares and traps to capture animals for the pot!'

Madame Ramsey nodded, seemingly quite unconcerned. 'And he does it well, does he not? He has his Cree friends to thank for his ability to ensure survival and I suspect, though he has never admitted it, that during his sojourns in the northwoods he has many times become lost and had cause to be grateful to his teachers. All decent human beings abhor cruelty, but ask yourself, my dear,' she urged softly, 'how many of us are such purists that we refuse to eat the flesh of fish, fowl or animal?'

Claire blushed, conscious that the mild rebuke was justified, and forced herself to stammer the very personal question.

'Didn't it bother you, marrying into a family possessing a strain of Indian blood?'

For a moment Rolf's mother looked so shocked Claire thought she was mortally offended. But then to her amazement she began to laugh, a merry trill of genuine amusement.

'I'm sorry, my dear,' she finally gasped, controlling her mirth with difficulty, 'but I had no idea that that old chestnut was still doing the rounds!

Who told you, for heaven's sake? The fable has cir-
culated for years around Montreal, but I never
dreamt it had hopped the Atlantic!'

'Fable...?' Remembering all the taunts she had
thrown at Rolf about his affinity with the Indians,
Claire's cheeks grew even more fiery. 'You mean it
isn't true?'

'Certainly not,' Madame chuckled. 'The rumour
erupted many years ago, spread, I suspect, by people
envious of Angus Ramsey's phenomenal success,
and was lent credence by his—at that time—unusual friendship with the Indians. The Ramseys
themselves are not blameless, they could easily have
proved the scandalmongers wrong, but either because of flattered egos or of tickled humour they
omitted to do so, thereby allowing the tale to be
accepted as true. Angus Ramsey was a literate and
extremely God-fearing man who would not have
dreamt of desecrating the family bible with a lie—
which is why his entry, written on the day of his
marriage to one Hannah Monroe, can never be
doubted.'

Dimly Claire was beginning to realise how wrong
she had been, how badly she had misjudged Rolf
Ramsey. The man his mother had described was a
total stranger to her, yet in an indefinable way she
felt she had met him in passing, that they were on
nodding terms, sharing a relationship that fate had
decreed should never be allowed to deepen.

The thought prompted a deep sense of loss, a
feeling of utter desolation that made Rolf's mother
gasp when she glimpsed it in Claire's eyes.

'I've treated him disgracefully,' Claire gulped,

white to the lips. 'I must go back and apologise, try
to explain.'

She had expected an overjoyed response, but felt
a terrible fear when Madame Ramsey frowned, her
expression pained. 'I wish you well, *chérie*, but I
suspect that it may be too late.'

'Why...? I don't understand...?' Fear thumped
a hard, heavy message upon Claire's heart.

'Every complaint you have made against my son
I have denied,' Madame admitted, the merry
twinkle completely absent from her eyes, 'except
one, a fault so strongly stitched into the fabric of
Ramsey life that no mother or wife has yet managed
to unpick it. "Never forget a favour—*never forgive
a slight.*" In common with all Ramsey men my son
is possessed of the devil's own pride, and I am very
much afraid that an absconded wife will have inflicted a burden of humiliation he will find impossible to forgive!'

CHAPTER THIRTEEN

No one who knew her would have recognised the wild-eyed girl speeding like a woman possessed along quiet roads leading towards the south tip of the island as the erstwhile cool, aloof Claire Foxdale.

But she was beyond caring what anyone thought —anyone, that was, except Rolf Ramsey, the man whose kisses had brought alive a sleeping beauty. When, during the silence that had fallen after his mother's prediction, she had remembered his promise: 'I shall return at nightfall' she had experienced the same sort of relief as a condemned man granted a last-minute reprieve, and in that same enlightening moment she had realised that life without Rolf would be no more than a living death. His mother had been understandably shocked when Claire had leapt from the couch and grabbed the car keys from the table. During her rush towards the car she had spared only a few breaths with which to toss incoherent words of explanation across her shoulder, but they had been enough to bring a smile of relief to her lips and a hopeful lilt to her voice as she had called out above the sound of the revving engine: 'Good luck, *chérie*, my love to you both!'

Instinct, or fate, guided Claire along the right roads, directed when she should turn off or carry straight on, so that when she eventually tumbled out of the car, parked it on the exact spot behind the outhouses where she had found it, and burst inside the cottage, she could hardly believe the hands of the clock that were insisting that only half of the afternoon had gone.

No definite plan had formulated in her mind, yet she began, feeling guided by unseen hands, to prepare for the homecoming of the '*dooiney mooar*' the head of the household. As confidently as if she had done the chore every day of her life, she scanned the depleted dresser and decided that there were sufficient ingredients left to provide a potato salad to accompany the fish Rolf would no doubt be bringing. Nimbly she peeled potatoes, placed eggs in the kettle and hooked it on to the *slouree* to boil. A weary head of celery was dunked into a mixture of vinegar and water to crisp, and as an afterthought she added green onions, in the hope that the marinade might help perk up their limp tails. Then she concocted a salad dressing from thinned canned milk seasoned with salt, pepper and mustard, but the problem of what to have for dessert defied solution. She was just about to settle for sugared grapefruit when inspiration struck. Sensing a spirit from the past leaning over her shoulder with a envious sigh, she unearthed a packet of gingerbread mix from the back of the dresser and carefully studied the instructions before mixing the contents. The batter smelled delicious, good as real, when she pushed it aside to turn her attention to the grapefruit. Slicing about a third from the top of each, she scooped out the fruit until she was left with two empty shells which she then filled with the cake batter before replacing the grapefruit lids. A foil container preserved from a previous instant meal would, she hoped, provide sufficient insulation when placed in the heart of the peat fire to prevent burning during the short time she had calculated the cakes would take to bake.

She worked feverishly, one eye upon a clock with hands that seemed suddenly to have begun racing around its yellowed dial, setting two places at the table with the prettiest crockery she could find, sparing precious minutes to arrange a centrepiece of wild flowers, then, as an afterthought, placing pewter candleholders, one either end of the table, with the intention of igniting the wicks immediately she received warning of Rolf's approach. Candlelight was romantic, and a lifetime of future happiness depended upon her ability to communicate to Rolf that his captive bride, far from being resentful, was now very willing.

Shadows were just beginning to lengthen when she decided that it was time to turn her attention upon her own appearance. She glanced around the room made cosy by flickering firelight; made welcoming by a table laden with salad tastefully arranged on a wooden platter, platefuls of crisply-baked bread, and ginger cakes that had turned out surprisingly well and were filling the kitchen with a spicy aroma guaranteed to put an even greater edge upon the appetite of a ravenously hungry man.

Blushing at the thought that Rolf's appetite might demand repletion from a very different kind of 'dish', she hunted through her still-unpacked

trousseau until she found the very special dress she
was seeking. With a murmur of satisfaction she
stroked her hand across material pink as a flamingo's
wing, downy as a feathered breast, then with shaking hands laid it across the bed before delving again
into the suitcases for items of underwear which,
when she tossed them on to the bed, fluttered
through the air and settled, transparent as moth-
wings, on top of her dress.

A shower took mere seconds, but she spent a long
time deciding which way to style her hair before
opting for the Indian braid that had so fascinated
Rolf he had been unable to resist a compulsion to
wind and unwind the golden rope, noosewise,
around her neck. With her hair parted severely
from the middle of her forehead and smoothed
tightly back into the confining plait her profile
stood out clear as a cameo, tender as a child's, yet
her grey eyes, lightly shadowed, held a fascinating
depth of mystique and lips, softly-rounded, quivering pink, were made tantalising by the type of
enigmatic smile made famous by the Mona Lisa.

The full-skirted dress, when she wriggled into it,
bared a deeply-hollowed cleavage, hugged a tiny
waist, then rustled past her knees with a satisfied
sigh that she involuntarily echoed when she looked
into the surface of a speckled mirror and decided
that she had never looked more approachable.

She had barely had time to light the candles and
blow out the flaming taper before the cottage door
opened and Rolf strode into the kitchen. He looked
nonplussed at the sight of her and stood for a moment, his back against the door, schooling indefin-

able emotions in eyes that looked storm-black beneath knitted brows tossed by wings of tousled hair.

'Hello...!' She had intended her voice to sound mellow as a flute and was annoyed when it came out highpitched as a tin whistle. Pulling herself together, she tried again. 'Did you manage a good catch?'

Speculatively, he eyed her, then unnerved her by striding mutely across the floor to drop a string of fish into a bucket.

His reaction was fiercely disappointing; Claire had expected a more definite response to her efforts, but without a sign of having noticed anything unusual he calmly began gutting the fish. All during dinner he remained silently uncommunicative, casting calculating glances upon the salad, the sourdough bread and the ginger cakes, sparing a longer look for the flowers and flickering candles yet at the end of it all saying not one surprised, appreciative nor even sarcastic word.

Gradually her waves of anticipation developed into a humiliating flood, rendering her so nervous as she sipped her milk that her hand jerked, slapping the liquid against her mouth so that she was forced to gulp more than she had intended. Rolf was morosely studying the contents of his plate, but looked up when she spluttered.

When eyes of fathomless black met startled grey he smiled, the swift teasing smile that invariably made her toes curl up. It disappeared as quickly as it had come, yet there was a hint of kindness behind the gravity of his tone.

'Your milky mouth and wide-eyed stare remind

me of a guilty schoolgirl caught out in some misdemeanour, Claire.' Then, infinitely delicate, he
prompted, 'Tell me, what have you been up to?
Have you done something you shouldn't while I
was away?'

'No, of course not,' she lied, hoping desperately
that he would not think to check the petrol gauge.

'You've remained in the cottage all day?' he insisted, forcing a second lie upon her conscience.

'Yes ... all day,' she stammered, a fiery blush
giving her away.

He shocked her by jumping to his feet with a
violence that sent a dish crashing to the floor.
Clamping hard hands upon her shoulders, he shook
her without mercy, gritting out the demand, 'Tell
me the truth, you lying little cheat! Shortly after I
left this morning I returned, my conscience plagued
by the reminder of your stricken face, determined
to apologise, to try to make my peace, only to find
that you'd taken off in the car the moment my back
was turned! There and then,' he blazed, 'I decided that I'd had enough, that a wife so lacking in
loyalty was not worth fighting for, so I went back
to my fishing,' his mirthless jerk of laughter hurt
more than the fingers hooked into her shoulders,
'and spent hours mulling over the problem of how
to fill an empty future. Can you wonder at my surprise when, instead of the empty cottage I was expecting, I returned to discover that you'd spent
hours preparing your version of the fatted calf and
that you'd tarted yourself up with the obvious intention of seducing your way back into my affections?' He felt her flinch, yet far from softening he

rammed home his advantage with the cruel taunt, 'Why did you come back, Claire, was it because you found out that Heywood no longer wants you—doesn't *dare* to want you—because of his fear of retribution? He's right to be afraid,' his voice dropped to a pitch of intense menace, 'because if he hadn't sent you packing I would have broken him both socially *and* physically!'

As he now intends to break me! she thought wildly, mesmerised by eyes burning in a face set expressionless as a mask. Further punishment was inevitable, but she could stand no more—loving him was punishment enough!

Desperation prompted the sort of guile that once she would have considered beneath contempt. With a low moan of distress she collapsed against him, deliberately allowing her smooth cheek to stroke across his chest. She heard his sharp intake of breath, then the second he relaxed his grip upon her shoulders she twisted out of reach, jerked open the door and fled blindly out of sight.

Night had fallen, but a bright full moon lit her way along the path leading to the cliff top, so she sped onward, stopping only once to kick off spindle-heeled shoes that were a hindrance when she leapt deep fissures veining the cliffs. But the folly of her flight hit her when she reached the edge and realised that there was nowhere else to go. Far below, waves were pounding the shore, the tide encroaching more than halfway up the path she had intended to use as an escape route. Knowing Rolf would be mere seconds behind in pursuit, she gasped a sob and flung herself down into a patch of shadow thrown by a crescent of rock and curled up tight, hoping against hope that he would not find her.

As she crouched, immersed in misery, she became conscious of a slight sound alien to the cry of the birds that were the cliff's only inhabitants. When it came again, a thin whimpering bleat, she stiffened, imagining Pete's ghost had returned to haunt her. Shaking off the fanciful notion, she crept on her hands and knees towards the edge of the nearest fissure and as the moon sailed high caught sight of a brown fleecy body teetering on the edge of a shelf halfway down the jagged chasm.

As it sensed her presence, the animal's bleating grew more insistent and as its head lifted she recognised a terrified lamb—Pete's twin sister.

If she had stopped to think she would have waited for Rolf who was almost certainly within yards of finding her, but the thought of the lamb starving without its mother chased all thought of caution from her mind. Flint-sharp rock cut into the soles of her feet as she zig-zagged a precarious path downwards towards the lamb using tufts of coarse grass for handholds, feeling with her stockinged feet for hollows deep enough to ensure she did not slip.

Luckily, the moon seemed curious and remained beaming light from above so that every outcrop of rock stood out distinctly as she worked her way down the chasm, narrow as the width of her shoulders, its shadow-shrouded depths pitted with boulders and frothing, hissing sea. Her feet were lacerated, her hands sore and bleeding by the time she reached the comparative safety of the ledge. Relief washed over her as she leant with her back against the rock face sucking in gulping breaths in an effort to steady her nerves and put stiffness into her wobbling knees.

On hestitant, spindly legs the lamb teetered towards her, mutely grateful, then once again gave a small despairing cry that went direct to Claire's heart.

'Come here, poor darling, let me warm you,' she coaxed, intending to pick the lamb up in her arms. But with a cold thrill of terror realisation struck. The ledge was too narrow for a forward bend, all it would allow was a sideways step either side, resulting in the fact that not only was the lamb trapped but so was she!

'Oh, Polly,' she quavered, appalled by her predicament, 'how did you get down here in the first place?'

Relieved of its loneliness, the lamb bleated joyfully, then, as if eager to show her how, it nosed its way behind a weatherbeaten tree clinging to the ledge and with a wriggle of its bottom and a flick of a plump tail it disappeared behind it. Thinking it might have fallen into a hole, Claire gasped and pulled the bush aside to discover a long foot-wide crack running right through the rock, splitting it in two. Helplessly she watched the lamb's hindquarters disappearing round a bend as the animal tripped along a well-trodden, obviously familiar path that was too narrow for all but the tiniest of creatures.

Then to make matters worse the moon became

engulfed by cloud, leaving the chasm black as pitch, cold and eerie as a tomb.

'Claire, where are you?' The blessedly-familiar voice was faint but nearing.

'Rolf, I'm here, halfway down a chasm, please come and get me!' she screamed, teetering on the edge of hysteria.

'Keep on shouting!' He sounded much closer. 'Loudly, so I can pinpoint your position!'

'Rolf ... Rolf ... I'm here ... I'm here ...!' Her words bounced against the walls but before reaching the surface seemed to fade into extinction 'Rolf,' she sobbed, pressing her cheek against cold, hard stone, 'give me one last chance to tell you how much I love you!'

Enshrouded in fear and pitch-black darkness, she lost all track of time, but encouraged by Rolf's frantic shouts she kept on calling him, knowing that somewhere up above he was searching every one of the many fissures hampered by darkness and by misleading sounds as her voice echoed through the honeycombed chasms. She was hoarse and numb with cold by the time his harsh, strained voice called out directly above her.

'Claire, are you down there!'

'Yes, yes!' she sobbed, 'please get me out of here!'

'*Sacré Coeur!*' The imprecation sounded strangled. 'Hang on for just five more minutes while I fetch a rope from the dinghy.'

She doubted if she could, but did not dare to say so because he sounded so angry, so full of impatience of her stupidity. For one insane moment she found herself wondering if it would not be better to allow herself to slip into oblivion rather than face his murderous mood of fury. But the choice was taken from her by a tersely shouted order.

'Tie the end of the rope around your waist and begin climbing slowly, a foot at a time, and don't worry, *chérie*, I won't let you slip!'

As if to his command the moon reappeared, spilling like a searchlight into the chasm. Claire looked up and as she saw Rolf's face, grim as the surrounding granite, her courage almost failed her.

'Well, what are you waiting for?' he bit savagely.

Sensing that he was incensed by her timidity, she swallowed back a plea that her hands and feet were numbed and swollen and, gritting her teeth to combat pain, she applied pressure to the rope and felt herself being hauled slowly to the surface.

It must have taken the strength of a madman to lift her dead weight at the end of a rope and yet at the same time to encourage calmly:

'Watch out for that outcrop on your left ... keep your head back ... hang on, Claire, you've almost made it!'

When her knees made contact with the ground she fell forward on to her face, sobbing her thankfulness, but he allowed her no respite. A thick sweater was pushed over her head and her arms thrust into sleeves so long that over a third of their length was left dangling past her fingertips. Then she was plucked from her feet into arms that promised strength without comfort and carried in grim silence along the cliff path, down the lane leading towards the cottage.

'It was the lamb's fault...' She wanted desperately to explain, but her head was spinning, her words jumbled and confused.

'Pete's dead, try to forget him,' Rolf ordered brusquely, obviously too angry to feign politeness.

Giving herself up to the exquisite agony of being held close against his heart, she tightened her arm around his neck and laid her head in the hollow of his shoulder, burrowing deeply so that she could sniff the clean, sea-tanged smell of him, could dare to ruffle her fingers ever so lightly through dark hair springing strongly above the nape of his neck.

Vaguely she wondered why his face was so white and haggard, why his lips were set in the line of a tightly-closed trap, why his bleak eyes stared straight ahead as if there was some goal he could not wait to reach.

When the cottage loomed he kicked open the door and stalked inside to lay her down upon the settle with a haste that made evident his wish to be rid of her.

'Take off those flimsy clothes,' he snapped, striding towards her bedroom, 'I'll search out something warmer.'

'I ... can't,' she choked, feeling the pain of her hands and feet escalating in the warmth of the kitchen.

'Why not?' He turned, seeming ready to argue, then expelled a hissing breath when he caught sight of her lacerated feet. '*Mon dieu*,' he whitened, 'what you lack in common sense you make up for in courage, *mon enfant*!'

She felt, in her warm, dreamy state, that at last

they were beginning to reach a better understanding as, with a tenderness that was an unbelievable contrast to his earlier manner, he set about bathing her hands and feet, cleaning the cuts with a touch like velvet before patting them dry and applying clean dressings. She did not feel in the least embarrassed when he undressed her, rubbed warmth into her limbs, then helped her into a thick, old-fashioned nightdress, showing such impersonal coolness she felt piqued.

Yet when he carried her to her bed and tucked the covers beneath her chin she felt able to express her gratitude with a shy smile.

'Thank you,' she said huskily, 'for all your kindness.'

Solemnly he stared down at her appealing face, so pale it looked lost among the cloud of hair spread out across her pillow.

'My aim was always to be kind, *ma chérie*,' his words had a ragged, tortured quality, 'but I've never quite managed it, have I? Will it help you to sleep better if I assure you that you never need fear me again, that you need never again risk your life to avoid the consequences of my foul temper? I intend giving you your freedom, Claire.' A muscle jerked violently in his cheek. 'Tomorrow I'm taking you home—afterwards, if you wish it, you need never set eyes on me again.'

CHAPTER FOURTEEN

PAIN kept her awake all night, the pain of a heart in torment, a mind numbed with despair. Incredibly, she and Rolf had achieved so many misunderstandings they had become strangers, strangers in love, two people who, each time they attempted to communicate, found themselves on different wavelengths.

She tossed feverishly, knowing that mere yards away Rolf would be stretched out in his sleeping bag staring at the rafters, plagued by a conviction that when she left the cottage she had run straight to Jonathan and, worst of all, that her fear of him had caused her to risk her life rather than face his anger. Dry sobs choked her throat; tears might have brought relief, but she was a well run dry—she, Claire Foxdale, who rarely showed her feelings, who had never been known to lose her temper, had, since becoming the wife of Rolf Ramsey, endured the extremes of every known emotion. He had been her creator, he had jerked her into pulsating life, taunted her into shows of temper, tears, misery and passion, yet now when she was fully alive and in need of him he was about to desert her! He had no right! she agonised resentfully, no right to kindle a fire and then leave it to dwindle into ashes! Her life depended upon his support, without him she might as well creep into the nearest grave...

She rose early, but even though the pain in her hands was minimal it took longer than she expected to fumble her way into a sleeveless top and a favourite pair of denims. It became evident immediately she stepped out of her bedroom that Rolf had been up since dawn. She saw his rolled-up sleeping bag and various other possessions set in a corner waiting to be stacked in the boot of the car. The fireplace had been swept clean, the *slouree* left dangling, the kettle whose singing had become a comfort was standing cold and empty on the hearthstone.

At the sound of his footsteps approaching the cottage Claire turned to the door to greet him, but her heart leapt, blocking her throat, when she saw him looking heartbreakingly handsome yet totally unfamiliar in a formal suit, pristine shirt, and an impeccably knotted tie.

His eyebrows rose, mutely questioning her casual outfit, yet his criticism was mild. 'Aren't you rather informally dressed for resuming your place in society?'

Stricken by his wry half-smile, she choked: 'I don't want to go—not yet!'

A shadow chased across his features; a lamp might have been turned off behind his eyes, leaving them blank pools of darkness. 'When surgery becomes necessary the cut should be swift,' he replied tightly. 'That way, the pain is less prolonged.'

Less prolonged, she thought wildly, *when every minute we're apart promises to be agony?*

Forcing herself to remain cool, she began fighting for her happiness and her sanity. Somehow she had to play for time, for just a few more hours during which she might be able to seize an opportunity to talk calmly and sensibly until all misunderstandings were dispelled. But Rolf must not be allowed to guess that he was being manoeuvred; success depended upon the time, the place, and his mood being just right.

'I enjoyed our sail so much,' she coaxed, grey eyes pleading, 'that I hoped we might make one last trip to the island. It needn't take long,' she forestalled his fierce objection, 'just a couple of hours, and afterwards,' she shrugged, 'well then, we'll go.'

Her shrug, her casual acceptance of their separation seemed to touch him on the raw. Controlling a wince that made her want to run into his arms to kiss his pain away, he acceded reluctantly to what he imagined was her last request. 'Very well, if you insist.' He cast a rueful glance at his suit. 'I suppose I'd better go and change.'

After a quick breakfast of slightly stale bread and fresh milk which to Claire tasted better than honey and nectar, they set off towards the shore. Before leaving the cottage Rolf had insisted upon examining her feet and changing the dressings but, solicitous though he was, he had had to agree that in the cold light of day the cuts were superficial and that with the aid of his ministrations they were healing up nicely.

Nevertheless, when they had walked a couple of hundred yards she decided she might chance a hobble, nothing theatrical enough to make him cancel their outing, just a barely perceptible limp to arouse his concern.

As she had calculated, he noticed immediately and without uttering a word he swung her into his arms, which was exactly where she had intended to be.

'Rolf,' she murmured, daring to brush her lips close to his cheek, 'can we stop on the cliff top? I want to show you how Polly managed to get stuck halfway down the chasm.'

He jerked to a halt, his face grim. 'Polly...?' he clamped. He seemed to be having trouble with his breathing, but as he had carried her so effortlessly the night before she suppressed a smile, knowing that his sharp intakes of breath and her own feather-weight were not connected.

'Pete's sister,' she explained gently. 'She was stranded on the ledge, but when I went down to help her the exasperating little animal made her exit through a gap just wide enough for her to squeeze through.'

'So you didn't...' he hesitated, his eyes narrowed upon the horizon.

'No, I did not deliberately jump into the chasm,' she spelled out carefully as she twisted a strand of his hair around her finger, thinking how darkly it contrasted against her fair skin—black as temper, strong and silky as his sun-kissed body.

'So I was wrong on that count,' Rolf conceded tersely, as if reluctant to absolve himself of blame. 'I'm glad.'

Wisely she allowed the subject to drop and concentrated upon the delight of being carried in his arms towards a sea sparkling with sunlight, capped with wavelets formed by a breeze that promised pleasure and excitement as they dared the stretch of water between island and mainland. One small hurdle had been safely jumped. Claire prayed her luck would hold out long enough to enable her to finish the course.

The sail was everything she had anticipated— breezy, exhilarating, demanding lots of co-operative action. During a moment of sheer enjoyment she loosened the pins in her hair and posed like a figure-head on the prow of a Viking longboat, enjoying the whip of the wind tossing and tousling fine strands into tangled golden floss. Unexpectedly she twirled a laughing face towards Rolf as they neared the island and was shocked to see his bleak expression, his rocky, outthrust jaw.

Making an effort to be pleasant, he forced a smile that progressed no further than an upward curling of his lip. 'I've never seen you looking happier,' he admitted stonily. 'If nothing else, your revived spirits prove that it was wrong of me to take you captive. I forced you to wear the chain of bondage,' he confessed bitterly, 'now justice has decreed that I should take my turn.'

She who is conceived in a cage yearns for a cage! Claire bit back the impulsive words from her lips. The time and the place were right, but Rolf's mood was far from perfect.

This time, when they landed, he held her only long enough to carry her ashore then, conveniently overlooking the injuries to her feet, he strode on ahead, his giant steps giving an impression of being eager for exercise. She strolled in his wake, respecting his need for solitude, feeling slightly ashamed of the way she was deliberately playing upon his susceptibilities. But the method she was using had been forced upon her, his emotions were so tightly clamped they had to be undermined even if the eventual reckoning should prove dangerous. His tensions could explode into a blast of either wrath or passion—either way, she had to know whether the basic emotion he felt for her was love or contempt.

She found him stretched flat on the sandy beach of the cove where they had swum on their last visit—was it really less than a week ago? He had stripped off his shirt and was lying face downward, his head supported on a forearm. He did not look up when she approached, but she could tell by muscles tensing beneath coffee-brown skin stretched silken taut across powerful shoulders that he was aware of her.

She sighed and slid down beside him, knowing it was time to re-commence her campaign. Scooping up a handful of sand, she let it trickle through her fingers into the hollow between his shoulderblades.

'I met your mother yesterday,' she told him, carefully casual. 'She's nice, I'd like to know her better.'

Rolf rolled over on to his back, staring his surprise. '*Maman?* How could you—she's still in Montreal!'

She shook her head. 'Our conversation was short,' she resumed solemnly, 'but I gathered that she was rather annoyed with you for refusing to postpone our wedding until she was able to arrange a flight from Canada. As it happened, she was offered a last-minute cancellation on a plane that arrived here on the day of our wedding. You can imagine how disappointed she was when she arrived at my father's house and discovered that she had missed us by just a couple of hours.'

As she talked Rolf had grown very still, and when he shot a question she sensed that his main object of interest was not his mother. 'You were absent from the cottage for only a few hours, yet you had time to meet and converse with my mother?'

'I went straight home and then straight back again,' she affirmed quietly.

'So you didn't...'

'... see Jonathan? No,' she assured him, her grey eyes steady, 'nor do I ever wish to see him again.'

She dropped her eyes, watching tiny particles of sand, agitated as her heartbeats, being tossed and teased by a playful breeze. Rolf's eyes were boring into her face, yet she dared not look up in case his expression should be projecting a message she did not want to read. Was her persistence becoming an embarrassment to him? Was it possible—her heart skipped a beat—that already her attraction had begun to wane and that he was seizing upon their clashes of temperament as a heaven-sent excuse to be rid of her?

But bitter self-condemnation ran heavily through his words when finally he grated, 'So I was wrong about the cause of your accident, and wrong again when I accused you of seeking out Heywood. You needn't continue pointing out what a swine I've been—I think I've got the message. Nevertheless, I refuse to apologise for what happened to your pet lamb—animals are fortunate,' he jerked, 'for them relief from pain is swift, but humans are forced to suffer interminably.'

He sprang to his feet, aggravated as a bear prodded by thorns. 'I'm going for a swim,' he growled, his anger seeming directed towards himself. 'After all that, I need not wait to hear you correct my one other fallacy—the idiotic notion that, in spite of your resistance, you might learn to hate me a little less!'

Left once more alone, Claire sank back on to the sand, a crumpled heap of dejection. However hard she tried she found it impossible to penetrate the prickly barrier Rolf had erected around himself. She was naïve, full of shy reserve, yet surely, if he had wanted to, he could have read encouragement in her tentative approaches. But perhaps—hope fluttered light as a butterfly's wings—her advances had not been explicit enough for a man grown used to rebuff, a man blinded by pride and plagued with guilty conscience. The solution seemed clear—she must intensify her campaign of seduction, do everything she could to prove to him that she loved him, short of actually spelling it out. To put her feelings into words was beyond her, for if her confession should leave him unmoved, worse still, *embarrassed*, then she would want to curl up and die!

She had had the foresight to bring a swimsuit, but as she fumbled her way into it she could not help but envy Rolf's lack of inhibitions, his insistence upon always swimming nude, and wishing she was bold enough to follow his example. Before her small store of courage could desert her, she ran down the beach and into the sea to swim towards the dark head bobbing above the water. But when he saw her coming he waved a warning and with powerful strokes began racing to meet her.

She was out of her depth, treading water, when his head surfaced and her eyes met his across a gulf of dividing sea.

'Farther out there's a strong undertow,' he clamped. 'Stay where the water is calm and there are no strong currents to harm you.'

'You could be warning me to stay out of your life,' she gasped, feeling the sea growing cold around her.

'Do you need to be warned?' She shivered, hating the remote quality of his tone. 'Does a slave hesitate to escape from a tyrant?'

She flicked a nervous tongue around spray-splashed lips and found the taste of sea-salt bitter. 'You're too self-critical, Rolf. People,' she hesitated, then forced herself to go on, 'people can sometimes be loved *because* of their faults, not merely in spite of them.'

'Love is a winged Cupid painted blind, eh, *chérie*?' He tossed back his head as if to laugh, then changed his mind. Swimming until he was within arm's reach of her, he pinched her chin between his thumb and forefinger to study her face with a solemnity that almost broke her heart. 'Let me look at you, *mon ange*, really look at you, for one last time, though there is little chance that I shall be allowed to forget what I have lost, because every grey sea will bring a reminder of your troubled eyes; on each sunlit day I'll recall the sight of your glorious hair being tossed by a playful breeze; on the face of every chastised child I'll see your drooping mouth and lashes heavy with tears. Console yourself with the thought that long after suffering has faded from your mind I shall still be doing penance, for once I considered love to be nothing more than sexual desire, but I now know that it's the only means of escape from the loneliness that plagues man throughout most of his existence!'

A second later he was gone, his image blurred by a mixture of stinging spray and slowly-welling tears.

With a heart dragging heavy as her feet, Claire heaved out of the water and toiled towards the shore. His goodbye had sounded so final it had left little room for hope. Yet somewhere deep inside her was stirring an emotion her Viking ancestors would have recognised, an urge to fight, a stubborn refusal to admit defeat. Last night, stranded halfway down a chasm, she had prayed for one last chance to tell him she loved him—*that chance would not have been given had Fate meant her to lose!*

Damp seeping in patches through dark blue denims was evidence that Rolf had pulled them on without bothering to dry his dripping limbs. His tanned, sea-flecked body, spreadeagled beneath the sun, remained immobile when Claire dropped to her knees a few yards distant. His hands were shading his eyes, but she could see stern lines compressing his mouth and a hatchet-sharp jawline.

'Rolf...' she gulped, then hesitated.

'Get dressed, Claire.' Her heartbeats faltered at the weariness of his tone. 'It's time I was taking you home.'

A tight knot of repression burst inside her.

'*No*...!' Casting dignity to the winds, she scrabbled on her knees towards him and flung her trembling, soaking body on top of his. 'I love you, Rolf,' she babbled wildly, staring a plea for kindness into his black, incredulous eyes. 'I love you ... I love you ... I love you...' Once she had said it she did not seem able to stop.

Muttering a hoarse imprecation, he rolled over to clasp her in a bear hug, silencing her with a hungry, draining kiss.

Revelling in the weight of his body crushing her, boneless, into the sand, Claire responded with a sensuality that amazed him, straining close, pressing urgent, bewitching kisses against every rapidly throbbing pulse, offering herself without reservation and thrilling with fascinated terror to the discovery that despite her puny strength she possessed the power to reduce a proud, arrogant male to the level of a trembling, pleading slave.

'Don't play tricks with me, Claire,' he growled a shaken, agonised threat against her warm, responsive mouth. 'I've taken just about all I can stand!'

'Sweet, stubborn voyageur,' she provoked tenderly, 'I thought you always took whatever you wanted?'

Long afterwards, she realised that life only began for her the moment she became possessed by a man, infinitely tender, savagely passionate, humble, yet inherently proud, the man who had taught her to hate—but who made a much better job of teaching her to love.

Drugged with ecstasy, she caressed him with her fingertips, loving every inch of his dark, silken skin.

'Darling Rolf,' she murmured, burying her lips against his strong, brown throat, 'never doubt my love again.'

A quiver weakened his powerful frame, but he spared an infinitesimal second to tease, complacent as a bear after a surfeit of honey, 'How could I, my proud princess, when you came to me begging, on your knees!'

Harlequin Presents...

The beauty of true romance...

The excitement of world travel...

The splendor of first love...

Harlequin Romances

The books that let you escape
into the wonderful world of romance!
Trips to exotic places...interesting
plots...meeting memorable people...
the excitement of love.... These are
integral parts of Harlequin Romances —
the heartwarming novels read by
women everywhere.

Many early issues are now available.
Choose from this great selection!

Choose from this list of Harlequin Romance editions.*

*Some of these book were originally published under different titles.